08/92

D1614629

BRITISH
TANK MARKINGS
AND NAMES

BRITISH TANK MARKINGS AND NAMES

The unit markings, individual names and paint colours of British armoured fighting vehicles, 1914-1945

B.T. White

Arms & Armour Press
London-Melbourne

T 7199

Published by
Arms and Armour Press,
Lionel Leventhal Limited,
2-6 Hampstead High Street,
London NW3 1QQ,
and at
4-12 Tattersalls Lane,
Melbourne, Victoria 3000.

British Library Cataloguing in Publication Data:
White, Brian Terence
British tank markings and names.
1. Tanks (Military science)—Identification marks
I. Title
358'.18   UG446.5

ISBN 0-85368-222-4

Acknowledgments. Many of the conclusions reached
during the preparation of this book are my own,
based on considerable research; notice of any
additions or corrections will be welcome. But, for
many of the facts contained in this material, I wish
to record my grateful thanks to the numerous
individuals and institutions, including regimental
historians and museum curators, who have helped in
various ways. In particular should be mentioned the
staff of the Imperial War Museum, and Colonel
Peter Hordern, Director of the Royal Armoured
Corps Tank Museum, Bovington Camp, Dorset,
whose encouragement makes studies of this kind so
rewarding and pleasant.
B. T. White, 1978

Edited by Tessa Rose.
Layout by Anthony A. Evans.
Typeset by Trade Linotype, Birmingham.
Printed in Spain by Mateu Cromo Artes Graficas,
S.A.

Overleaf:
Two Mark I Cruisers of 'C' Squadron, Royal Tank Regiment in the Desert, 1940. They are
painted in the three-colour radiating lines system; the lightest colour (in side view) is on the
rear half of the track-guard, the medium shade is on the upper hull and lower edge of the
turret and the darkest colour extends over much of the turret including, probably, the
roof. (I.W.M.)

CONTENTS

INTRODUCTION

The giving of individual names to British armoured cars and tanks is a tradition going back to the earliest times when first they were used in combat. In France, before the end of 1914, a number of Commander Samson's Royal Naval Air Service armoured cars had already been given the names of some of the unit's recent battle honours. The development of tanks owed much to the inspiration of the Royal Naval Air Service—it should be remembered that one of the alternative names for Mother, the direct prototype of the first tanks to enter service, was H.M.L.S. (His Majesty's Land Ship) *Centipede*. Naval Volunteers together with men from many units of the Army helped to man the tanks of the Heavy Section, Machine Gun Corps—Heavy Section was renamed Heavy Branch in November 1916—when it first saw action on 15 September 1916. Most of the tanks at this time bore individual names prefixed by H.M.L.S.

The Royal Navy has a long and honourable tradition of handing down ships' names. By custom, ships in the same class often have names associated with one another and, for the smaller vessels in particular, often shared the same initial letter. The British Army, for its part, has for long favoured territorial designations —as opposed to mere numerals—for its regiments. Also, of course, most British regiments have acquired nicknames during the course of their history—some laudatory, some humourous and some unprintable! All these sources, and many others, infinitely inventive, can be traced in the names given to British armoured fighting vehicles from 1914 to the present time.

Throughout the history of the Tank Corps (as the Heavy Branch, Machine Gun Corps was renamed) the naval tradition of giving names in classes, usually with the same initial letter, was generally, although by no means rigidly, followed. When British Cavalry regiments were first mechanized between the two World Wars, they also, in most cases, named their armoured cars or tanks, although, as would be expected, the names tended to have a much more 'horsey' flavour than those of the Royal Tank Corps. The present writer is not qualified or able to investigate the psychology behind the choice of particular

names, but he likes to think that at least one tank name (of 6th Battalion, Tank Corps, 1917-18) summarizes the morale of the British soldier—*Fums Up*. Many of the customs of the British Army were also adopted by armies of the British Commonwealth countries. Included in these customs was the naming of AFVs, although naturally the names chosen by them had a local flavour.

The whole subject of regimental names for armoured fighting vehicles is a wide one, and one that is little recorded, often earning only a line or two in printed regimental histories. Although many sources (mentioned under Acknowledgments in this book) have been tapped, a great deal remains to be recorded, and the author will be pleased to learn of any fresh information.

Markings (apart from names) on British armoured fighting vehicles were evolved, and added to, for various purposes as the need arose. The tactical function remained throughout both World Wars, and it is interesting to note that, towards the end of the Second World War, there was a reversion in some units to the early Tank Corps practice (during the First World War) of showing large individual numbers for tanks. Various national markings used at different times seem to have had only one thing in common—a dislike of them by tank crews, mainly because they were as conspicuous to the enemy as to friends and often provided good aiming points for unfriendly guns. The British Second World War system of unit code signs tied in with the formation sign was a fairly good one. The numbers used often followed no logical pattern and were, it may be assumed, sometimes shuffled so as to deceive the enemy. The figure 40, for example, was used for the senior regiment in an armoured brigade in the Middle East in 1942, whereas in the United Kingdom it was the code number for a divisional headquarters.

In general, it can be said of individual names and almost all other embellishments (except the W.D. number) on armoured fighting vehicles that these were shown at their best, and in the form most approved by higher authorities, when the unit was not in action. In periods of action there were often much more

pressing matters to attend to than repainting markings, and frequently there was no time at all to paint them on replacement AFVs. Again, Commonwealth practice followed that of Britain in the range and form of AFV markings, the chief differences being noted in the section dealing with this subject (see page 64).

Camouflage painting of armoured fighting vehicles has ever been a controversial subject. Ideas over the years have ranged from an array of bright colours to a single drab colour—with regular changes of mind by the War Office and frequent examples of formation, unit and even squadron commanders who felt they knew better than the War Office, and perhaps did. It would be almost impossible to record all the permutations of colour and pattern used on British and Commonwealth armoured fighting vehicles between 1914 and 1945; but the main recommended systems, and some of the more notable unit variations, have been mentioned or illustrated here. Comment on camouflage colours in the captions to the photographs is confined to what can be said with some degree of confidence. In the absence of technical detail (such as the type of film used) it is almost impossible to say, from a photograph alone, if a tank is, for example, bronze-green or khaki-brown. Even where a unit is known to have used a certain colour at a certain time, the actual appearance of a particular vehicle—because of weathering, the result of combat, or the addition of dust or mud—may be changed out of all recognition. Despite this, in the colour plates, the artist has tried to give an impression of the appearance of the AFVs as they were; but for those who wish to go back to the original paint specification, British Standards references have been quoted, where these are known, in the relevant section of the book.

AFV NAMES

1. Royal Naval Air Service Armoured Car Division

The force of armoured cars that was formed in 1914, to protect Royal Naval Air Service bases in Belgium and northern France and to support aircraft operations, was subsequently expanded into the R.N.A.S. Armoured Car Division. Some of the first armoured cars specially built for this force, under the overall command of Commander C. R. Samson, R.N., were given names of places where earlier actions had taken place; examples are *Aniche, Douai* and *Cassel*. These names were painted in largish white letters on the rear of the hulls.

The R.N.A.S. armoured car squadrons formed later (from late 1914 onwards) normally carried the squadron number, the section letter and the number of the car in the section; these were painted prominently on the sides and/or front and rear of the vehicles. In addition, most, if not all, squadrons gave names to their vehicles. These were usually on small metal plates or painted in small letters at the rear of the armoured cars' chassis or on the side lockers near the back. The first four squadrons (each equipped with twelve Rolls-Royce armoured cars and three Seabrook heavy armoured cars) set a tradition, which was later followed by the Tank Corps, of using the letter equivalent to the squadron number. Examples of names used are *Alexandria, Amethyst, Anne Gallant, Alert, Active, Adamant, Assault* and *Alliance* (No. 1 Squadron); *Bustler, Busy, Bouncer, Biter, Bulldog, Bloodhound, Borzoi, Black Joke, Banterer* and *Bold*—the last three being Seabrooks (No. 2 Squadron); *Chesapeake, Cockatrice, Columbine, Camilla, Cordelia* and *Caradoc* (No. 3 Squadron); *Decoy, Diana, Dasher, Doris* and *Delight* (No. 4 Squadron). For no obvious reason, No. 6 Squadron, equipped with Lanchester instead of Rolls-Royce armoured cars, used names beginning with 'G', such as *Gannet* and *Good Hope*. In 1915, most of the R.N.A.S. armoured cars were handed over to the Army, which reorganized them into Armoured Motor Batteries of the Machine Gun Corps. Despite this reshuffle the original names used by the cars were in some cases retained.

2. Tank Corps

The R.N.A.S. Armoured Car Division provided much of the initiative and technical expertize in developing the first tanks, and numbers of naval officers and ratings were transferred to the Army to help form the Heavy Branch, Machine Gun Corps (renamed the Tank Corps in July 1917). The tanks made their initial appearance on the Somme in September 1916; and 'C' and 'D' Companies (both comprising four sections of six tanks) were the first to see battle. These two Companies used names beginning with the Company letters. No. 1 section of 'C' Company bore the names of wines, such as *Chartreuse, Champagne, Cognac, Chablis, Cordon Rouge* and *Creme de Menthe*. One of the few tanks to be photographed in this first battle (Flers-Courcellette) was H.M.L.S. *Clan Leslie*, (a Mark I tank) C.19 of No. 4 section. Some

▲1 ▼2

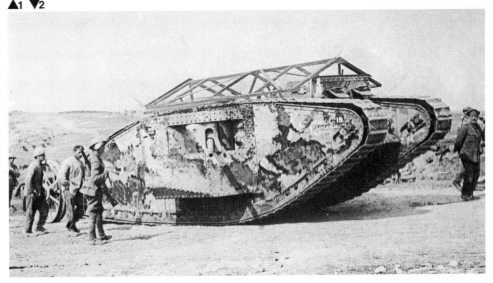

1. *Good Hope*—a Lanchester armoured car of No. 6 Squadron, R.N.A.S. Armoured Car Division in 1915. (Courtesy F. S. Hutton-Stott)

2. Mark I Male tank *Clan Leslie* (C.19) of 'C' Company, H.B.M.G.C. during the Battle of Flers-Courcelette, 15 September 1916—the first battle in which tanks took part. This tank has the original red, green, blue and brown camouflage scheme. (I.W.M.)

No. 16 Company (Sections 1-4)		No. 17 Company (Sections 5-8)		No. 18 Company (Sections 9-12)	
F.1	*Firespite*	F.21	*Five Knights*	F.41	*Fray Bentos*
F.2	*Frivolous*	F.22	*Flying Fox*	F.42	*Faun*
F.3	*Frolic*	F.23	*Foggie*	F.43	*Fritz Phlattner*
F.4	*Flirt*	F.24	*Frisky*		
F.5	*Firefly/Fervent*	F.25	*Fums Up*	F.45	*Fiducia*
F.6	*Feu d'Artifice*	F.26	*Fearless*	F.46	*Fay*
F.7	*Feu de Ciel*	F.27	*Fighting Mac*	F.47	*Foam/Faralone*
F.8	*Freemason*	F.28	*Formidable*	F.48	*Fiara*
F.9	*Feu Follet*			F.49	*Fairy*
F.10	*Feu d'Enfer*	F.30	*Flaming Fire*	F.50	*Fay*
F.11	*Fizyama*	F.31	*Fearnought*	F.51	*Fortuna*
F.12	*Friar Tuck*			F.52	*Foam II*
F.13	*Falcon*			F.54	*Festina Lente*
F.15	*Fifinella*			F.55	*Fly-by-Night*
F.16	– (wireless tank)	F.36	*Furious*	F.56	*Fly Paper/Fan Tan*
F.17	*Follow the Crowd* (supply tank)	F.37	*Ferocious*	F.57	*Flanders Fly*
		F.38	*Firefly*	F.58	*Fly Flapper*
F.19	*Fill Up* (supply tank)	F.39	*Formosa*		

Supply and wireless tanks at Cambrai (un-named): F.S.1, F.S.2, F.21, F.37, F.W.1, F.W.3

18. - ZILLEBEKE. - Tanks "*Appolyon*" et "*Aberdonia*"
"*Appolyon*" and "*Aberdonia*" Tanks

▲3 ▼4

contemporary 'D' Company tanks included the rather cosmopolitan collection of *Dolphin*, *Donner Blitzen* (sic) (German for 'thunder and lightning') and *Dinnaken* (Scots for 'don't know').

In December 1916, the first four companies were expanded into battalions, each comprising four companies of twelve tanks. Further new battalions were raised as the war progressed, until, by the Armistice, the Tank Corps was composed of eighteen battalions. The practice became almost universal in the Tank Corps of giving names that corresponded to the battalion letter. The letters were changed to their equivalent numbers in the spring of 1918, although all those at Cambrai in November seem to have conformed to 'B' names. Some of the tanks of 'B' (2nd) Battalion were exceptions to the rule: in June 1917 No. 5 Section of 5th Company included *Lucifer*, *Our Emma* and *Rumblebelly*. No doubt there were also exceptions in other battalions, but in most cases the system was observed. When painted on, the position and form the names took varied considerably. This depended to some extent on which was considered of more tactical use: the name or the battalion number. In 'B' Battalion at Cambrai in 1917, for example, the name appeared on the back of the hull at the top, with the battalion tank number (B 28 for example) below it, and also repeated on the sides of the front 'horns'. In 'C' Battalion the name appeared on the front glacis plate of the hull, below the driver's and commander's visors. Names in 'H' Battalion were carried on the 'horns' near the front.

Space does not allow the quoting of examples from all battalions of the Tank Corps (and, in some instances records are thin), but an almost complete list for 'F' (6th) Battalion, from August to November 1917, is given in Table 1. These names were not continued when the unit reorganized as a Light Battalion equipped with Mark A Mediums. The famous Mark A tank *Musical Box* was with the 6th

3. Knocked-out Mark IV tanks of 'A' Battalion, Tank Corps, at Zillebeeke, Belgium — Third Ypres battle, July 1917. The names *Appolyon* and *Aberdonia* are just visible on the hull sides near the drivers' cabs.

4. A rear view of B 28 (*Black Arrow*) a Mark IV Male tank of 'B' Battalion, Tank Corps, in 1917.

5. *Firespite II* (F.1), a Mark IV Female tank of 'F' Battalion, training in October 1917. (I.W.M.)

6. The Mark IV Female tank on display at the Royal Armoured Corps Tank Museum. Although freshly painted, this is believed to have been the original F.4 of 'F' Battalion, Tank Corps. T179 is a post-war number, but one not in the regular series used later.

▲5 ▼6

7. *Hydra II* of 'H' Battalion, Tank Corps, after being knocked-out in 1917.

8. A temporarily abandoned Rolls-Royce armoured car of a Light Armoured Motor Battery in France. The distinctive zig-zag camouflage scheme was also used for artillery. (I.W.M.)

9. The battalion to which this Mark A Medium belongs is not identified, but the name *Julian's Baby* can be seen on the front and also on the side of the cab below the W.D. number A 217. (I.W.M.)

▲10

▲11 ▼12

10. L.28 of 'L' Battalion, Tank Corps, in German possession. The W.D. number 4556 is on the hull side near the rear.

11. HMAC *Harvester* and its crew—the 1920 Rolls-Royce Pattern armoured car is shown at the time of its service with the 1st Armoured Car Company, Tank Corps, in Iraq in 1921. Shortly before this the car had belonged to a Light Armoured Motor Battery. (Tank Corps Journal)

12. Mark II India Pattern light tanks of the 2nd Light Tank Company, R.T.C., on patrol near the Khyber Pass in about 1936. The number 'N' on the turrets denotes No. 3 section; the other sections adopted the letters 'T' and 'I' respectively. These tanks probably used a light khaki-brown camouflage scheme.

13. A Carden-Loyd Mark VI Carrier belonging to 4th Battalion, R.T.C., doing duty as a light tank. The W.D. number is shown on the hull side along with the unit's eye symbol and number.

14. *Blair Atholl*, a Mark I medium tank of 'B' Company, 2nd Battalion, R.T.C., at manoeuvres during the 1930s. The civil registration mark ME 9900 is clearly visible and the W.D. number, which is not shown on the front, is T.27.

15. A Mark II Medium of 5th Battalion, Royal Tank Corps, being loaded on to a Scammell tank transporter. The battalion number, in white, can just be seen behind the civil registration mark (ME 9979). Note the dark line around the hull and the geometric tactical sign, which then denoted 'B' Company, on the back. (Scammell Lorries Ltd.)

▲13

▲14 ▼15

Battalion in 1918, but there is no evidence that names were in general use for 6th Battalion Mediums during the war.

The Aug.—Nov. 1917 list is a combined one of those tanks mentioned in the unit's history as having taken part in the Third Ypres (August 1917) and/or Cambrai (November 1917) battles. Tanks bearing the same battalion number, but renamed at the time of Cambrai, are shown with both names. In many cases new tanks bore both the old numbers and names, although the latter usually had the suffix 'II' (one exception at Cambrai was F.37 which was named *Ferocious III*). In a few cases at Cambrai the same name was perpetuated in a tank with a different number. The Mark IV Female at the Tank Museum, Bovington, is painted as F.4 of 'F' Battalion, and it is believed that this is the original tank to bear this number.

The Tank Corps size was greatly reduced after the First World War, and only the Armoured Car Companies (most of which were stationed in India and subsequently re-equipped and, in many cases, renamed Light Tank Companies) used names fairly consistently. (In 1923 the Corps was granted the prefix 'Royal', and became The Royal Tank Corps.) The 4th Battalion continued the use of their 'D' names, and were later joined in this practice by 3rd Battalion, which revived some of the wartime names for its various Vickers medium tanks and Carden-Loyd Tankettes. 2nd Battalion also re-adopted some wartime names for its 'B' Company, although its 'A' and 'C' Companies used names beginning with 'A' and 'C' respectively. On the whole, this latter system was fairly widely adopted by many units in the Second World War. 5th Battalion, Royal Tank Corps, does not appear generally to have named its tanks; instead it was the only one to revive the wartime practice of showing battalion tank numbers, such as E.48, in large white characters. For 2nd Battalion's medium tanks, the W.D. number (without the 'T' prefix) was shown in large white figures on the front, rear and sides. In the inter-war period geometric tactical signs of the general type, later standardized during the Second World War, were introduced.

3. The Royal Tank Regiment (Second World War)

The Royal Armoured Corps was created on 4 April 1939 to include the Royal Tank Corps (renamed The Royal Tank Regiment), cavalry and mechanized yeomanry regiments. During 1939 The Royal Tank Regiment was increased from eight (the 7th and 8th were formed in 1937 and 1938) to twenty battalions by the formation of twelve Territorial battalions (mostly converted from infantry) of the Regiment.

▲16

▲17 ▼18

Between 1940 and 1941, four further battalions were added: the 9th, 10th, 11th and 12th. The new battalions of The Royal Tank Regiment usually adopted the traditional practice of giving all their tanks names beginning with one letter which corresponded to the battalion number. As the Territorial battalions were numbered from 40th onwards, however, the system could not be followed exactly. All the new R.T.R. battalions, from the 7th onwards, were raised as infantry tank battalions. In 1940, the 23rd and 24th Army Tank Brigades (which were composed of 40th, 46th, 50th and 41st, 45th and 47th Battalions of The Royal Tank Regiment) were incorporated in the new 8th Armoured Division; these six battalions did not follow the general R.T.R. naming system. By 1941, the list for The Royal Tank Regiment was as follows:

1st Battalion: In 1940 the names of the cruiser and light tanks began with the letter 'A'. This system was abandoned later, and various names, often humourous, were used. (Details of those used in 1944 are given in Table 2.)

2nd Battalion: Details are not available, but the inter-war system mentioned above may have been continued. (This old system was certainly resumed after the Second World War, examples between 1947 and 1953 being *Agincourt*, *Badger* (Squadron Leader) and *Cambrai*.)

3rd Battalion: All tank names began with the letter 'C'. Some were inherited from the First World War, but new names were also used. One innovation was the use of American place-names, such as *Connecticut* and *Columbia* for American-built Stuart light tanks.

4th Battalion: All tank names began with the letter 'D'; examples are *Derwent*, *Dreadnought*, *Dolphin*, *Devil*, *Deoch* and *Destroyer*. In France, during 1939-40, Mark I infantry tanks also carried the traditional eye insignia of the battalion on their turrets.

16. 1st Battalion, R.T.R., Mark VI light tanks on patrol in the Egyptian Desert, 1940. The two nearest tanks—*Aberdeen* and *Alsace*, both of 'C' Squadron—are carrying the unit code number 24 (in white on a red square) and civil registration marks, which were still in use at this stage of the War. (I.W.M.)

17. *Columbia IV*, a Stuart of 3rd Troop, 'A' Squadron, 3rd Battalion, Royal Tank Regiment—at this time in the 4th Armoured Brigade, 7th Armoured Division—being inspected in the Desert in 1942. The tank's dark disruptive camouflage patterns have been sprayed on. (I.W.M.)

18. *Deoch*, a Mark I infantry tank of 4th Battalion, Royal Tank Regiment, in France, 1940. The number 1874 on the side of the hull is this Battalion's mobilization serial number. (I.W.M.)

▲19 ▼20

19. *Skyraker* (alias *The Princess*) of 1st Battalion, Royal Tank Regiment, in Normandy, 1944. The unit mobilization number is on the glacis plate of this Crusader AA tank, just above the LST number. (I.W.M.)

20. A dug-in Cromwell tank of either 1st or 5th Battalion, Royal Tank Regiment, near Sittard, Holland, in January 1945. The 7th Armoured Division sign appears on the left of the rear plate, and the 22nd Armoured Brigade sign (a stag's head) immediately above the unit code sign (52 or 53). (I.W.M.)

21. Infantry, having successfully hitched a lift, climbing aboard *Charlestown I*, a Sherman of 'C' Squadron, 3rd Battalion, Royal Tank Regiment, in Normandy. (I.W.M.)

22. *Durban*, leading a line of Matildas of 4th Battalion, Royal Tank Regiment, in the Western Desert. (I.W.M.)

23. Two Regimental Headquarters vehicles, a Mark IB scout car and a Stuart, of 5th Battalion, Royal Tank Regiment, in the Desert in 1942. On the scout car, the small jerboa above the unit code number 67 (on a red square) represents the 4th Armoured Brigade, and the large jerboa the 7th Armoured Division. On the tank, the name *Exe* and the R.HQ diamond on the turret are in blue and the W.D. number (T 37783) is in white. Both vehicles are in an overall sand colour. (I.W.M.)

24. *Fly Flapper*, a First World War name revived for this Mark I cruiser of the 6th Battalion, Royal Tank Regiment, being given a 'spring clean' by its crew in Libya, 1940. (I.W.M.)

▲21 ▼22

▲23 ▼24

25. *Grimsby* (W.D. No. T 10085) is the first in this formidable line of Matildas of 7th Battalion, Royal Tank Regiment, in the Desert in 1941. These tanks were painted in the three-colour scheme of radiating straight lines. (I.W.M.)

5th Battalion: All tank names began with the letter 'E'; examples—ranging from Cruiser Mark Is in 1940, through Stuarts used in the Desert, to Shermans in Normandy—are *Elephant* (R.HQ), *Eley* ('A' Squadron) and *Em-an-Vee* ('C' Squadron).

6th Battalion: All tank names began with the letter 'F'. Some of the old First World War names were used, examples being *Fly Flapper*, *Fray Bentos* and *Formidable*.

7th Battalion: All tank names began with the letter 'G', and a high proportion of these were old 'G' Battalion names used in the First World War; examples are *Grumble*, *Gossip*, *Giggle*, *Gnome* and *Gnat*. The 7th was destroyed in 1942 at Tobruk, and the 10th Battalion The Royal Tank Regiment, was renamed 7th in April 1943. Despite this, the 'J' names used by the 10th were retained until the end of the War. One example is *Jinks*, which was the

26. *Fray Bentos*, a famous name from the First World War carried by this Crusader of the 6th Battalion, Royal Tank Regiment, knocked-out in the Desert in 1941 near Sidi Resegh.

Commanding Officer's Humber scout car in 1944.

8th Battalion: All tank names began with the letter 'H'; examples are *Hake, Hector, Hengist, Honiton, Hull, Huddersfield* and *Hobo*.

9th Battalion: All tank names began with the letter 'I'; examples (all Churchill tanks, 1942) are *Imp, Impetuous, Irate* ('A' Squadron); *Ivan, Immortal, Invincible, Iroquois* ('B' Squadron).

10th Battalion: All tank names began with the letter 'J'; examples are *Julian, Jumbo, Jessie* (1st, later 3rd, Troop of 'A' Squadron).

11th Battalion: No definite evidence has been found that names beginning with 'K' were used, although it is likely that they were early on in the War. However, the Buffaloes (tracked landing vehicles) with which the Battalion was equipped early in 1945, for amphibious operations in Holland and Germany, were all given names beginning with the letter 'S'—towns, birds and animals predominating. By the time of the River Elbe crossing in March 1945 this Battalion had adopted the system used by the Assault Regiments, Royal Engineers, of showing large numbers and letters indicating the troop of the squadron, and the position of the

▲27 ▼28

tank in the troop. Examples of names and tactical markings are *Southwark* (1B); *Swan* (1C); *Salamander* (3B); *Squirrel* (4A); *Stork* (4C); and *Sheldrake* (4E).

12th Battalion: All tank names began with

27. The R.HQ Humber scout car heading this line of vehicles of the 7th Battalion, Royal Tank Regiment, in Normandy, 1944, bore a name (*Junior*) that had been used by the 10th Battalion, R.T.R., before it was renamed the 7th. Note that the 7th's mobilization serial number (1875) has been adopted, along with the red tactical signs appropriate to the senior regiment (with 9th Battalion, R.T.R. and 141st Regiment, R.A.C.) in the 31st Tank Brigade. (P.N.A.)

28. *Indus*, a Churchill I of 'B' Squadron, 9th Battalion, Royal Tank Regiment, on an exercise in the United Kingdom early in 1942. (I.W.M.)

29. Churchill IIIs of the 12th Battalion, Royal Tank Regiment in Tunisia. The name *Largs* can just be seen in front of the 'B' Squadron tactical sign on the turret side of the nearest tank. (I.W.M.)

30. A Buffalo IV (LVT Mark IV), belonging to 11th Battalion, Royal Tank Regiment, with a cargo of German prisoners in Holland in the winter of 1944. The name *Slough* is shown on the upper side of the hull. The unit code sign 67, which is not visible, is a carryover from the number used for the senior tank regiment in the tank brigade of a mixed division in 1942.

▲29 ▼30

the letter 'L'; examples are *Lydd, Leander, Largs, Ludlow, Liss* and *Lily*.

40th Battalion: Names of tanks were chiefly those of British warships. In 'A' Squadron, names began with the letter 'A'; examples are *Ajax, Antelope* and *Ardent*. However, it seems that those of Regimental Headquarters and 'B' and 'C' Squadrons followed no particular letter; examples are *Scorpion* (R.HQ), *Penelope* (B) and *Mohawk* (C). This unit, plus the 46th and 50th Battalions, formed the famous 23rd Armoured Brigade (originally in the 8th Armoured Division) for the greater part of the Second World War. (For convenient reference, the other units of this Brigade follow immediately below.)

46th Battalion: This Battalion was formed from The Liverpool Welsh Territorial infantry battalion. The personnel wore a dragon sleeve badge, and in 1942 the Commanding Officer's pennant (now in the Tank Museum, Bovington) was a red Welsh dragon on a green background. Tank names began with the letter 'C' for Regimental HQ, 'D' for 'A' Squadron, 'E' for 'B' Squadron, and 'F' for 'C' Squadron. Many of these names were of British warships; examples of some 'C' Squadron tanks are *Faulkner, Furious, Fiji, Formidable, Firedrake* and *Falcon*.

50th Battalion: Tank names for Regimental HQ began with the letter 'H'; examples are *Hood* and *Hawkins*. 'A' Squadron used the letter 'R', and names ranged from *Rollicker II* and *Roysterer II* (for Mark VIC light tanks early in the War) to *Reliance, Respond, Redoubtable* (Valentines in North Africa) and *Relic* (a Sherman in Italy). 'B' Squadron adopted the letter 'B'; examples are *Broke* and *Badger*. And 'C' Squadron used the letter 'C'; examples are *Cotswold, Cheviot* and *Chiltern* (11th Troop Shermans in Sicily).

41st Battalion: With the 45th and 47th Battalions Royal Tank Regiment, this unit formed the 24th Armoured Brigade of the 8th Armoured Division. Regimental HQ tanks' names began with the letter 'R'; examples are *Regain, Regina, Rio* (the Regimental Intelligence Officer's tank) and *Russia*, with *Rover* as one of the scout cars. Names in 'A' Squadron began

31. Valentines of the 40th Battalion, Royal Tank Regiment and a distant Matilda Scorpion flail tank in Tunisia. Although its name is indistinguishable, the nearest tank (W.D. No. T 16319) shows clearly the 23rd Armoured Brigade sign and unit code sign 40 on the nose plate. (I.W.M.)

32. A Valentine in Tunisia laden with Highland infantrymen. This tank is *Respond* of 'A' Squadron, 50th Battalion, Royal Tank Regiment, belonging to the 23rd Armoured Brigade. (I.W.M.)

▲32

with the letter 'A'; 'B' Squadron with the letter 'B'; and 'C' Squadron with the letter 'C'. A number of the names in the latter Squadron had a distinctly Iberian flavour as the following examples show: *Cadiz, Cavez, Corunna, Cortez* and *Caldos*. The Battalion was temporarily renamed 'The Scorpion Regiment', when equipped with flail tanks in North Africa; appropriately, at this time a scorpion badge was carried on pennants.

45th Battalion: All names were originally those of ships, but later these were varied. 'A', 'B' and 'C' Squadrons used names that followed the squadron letter; examples are *Alaric, Attilla* (sic), *Bannockburn, Broke, Culloden* and *Cyclops*.

47th Battalion: Regimental HQ tanks bore names beginning with 'D', while 'A', 'B' and 'C' Squadron names followed the squadron letter.

42nd Battalion: All tank names began with the letter 'P'; examples are *Pasadena* and *Phantom* (Matildas in the Western Desert). This Battalion was re-formed as a Territorial unit after the War, and in 1953 the more unusual idea of using the names of public houses was in operation.

43rd Battalion: All tank names began with the letter 'S'. This system was carried from the Matildas of 1941, through the Churchills received later, to the experimental vehicles used with the 79th Armoured Division. Examples (for Churchills in 33rd Tank Brigade) are *Saracen, Spokesman* and *Samson* (1st Troop, 'A' Squadron); *Shampoo, Shingle* and *Shaver* (9th Troop, 'B' Squadron).

44th Battalion: All tank names began with the letter 'R'. Those in 'A' Squadron all commenced 'Ra . . .' (for example, *Rajah, Ramadan, Racket*; 'B' Squadron 'Re . . .' (for example, *Restive, Revenge, Rex*); 'C' Squadron 'Ro . . .' (for example, *Romeo, Rover*); and R.HQ 'Ru . . .' (such as *Rustler*, the Adjutant's Sherman tank in 1944).

48th Battalion: All tank names began with the letter 'T' beginning with Churchills in the United Kingdom, and continuing right through to the Italian campaign where *Texan, Titan* and *Tumult* were the 3rd Troop of 'A' Squadron. After the Battle of San Fortunato in 1944, a Canadian maple leaf device was carried on the tanks and on the uniforms of the crews.

49th Battalion: In 1941, when this unit was equipped with Matildas, tank names for Regimental HQ began with the letter 'E'; 'A' Squadron with 'F'; 'B' Squadron with 'G'; and 'C' Squadron with 'H'. The 49th Battalion, Royal Tank Regiment became the 49th Armoured Personnel Carrier Regiment (equipped with Kangaroos) in 1944. At this time, names appear to have been used more or less at

▲33

▲34 ▼35

▲36 ▼37

33. A Matilda of 42nd Battalion, Royal Tank Regiment, in the Western Desert in late 1941 showing its white/red/white recognition signs on both turret and hull. This is W.D. number T 6968, *Phantom*, possibly of 10th Troop, from the number visible just below the steel helmets hanging on the turret. (I.W.M.)

34. *Shepherd*, *Sheepdog* and *Shylock*, Churchill IIs belonging to 'B' Squadron of the 43rd Battalion, R.T.R., 33rd Tank Brigade, which at this time (1942) formed part of the 3rd (Mixed) Division. The divisional sign has been deleted by the censor from the left-hand rear track-guard, but tactical, recognition and unit code (67 in white on a brown square) markings are still showing. (I.W.M.)

35. A Sherman of the 2nd Troop of 'B' Squadron, 44th Royal Tank Regiment, at the Sangro crossing in Italy, 1944. The name *Rex* is on the hull side just below the Browning machine-gun. Compare the size of the red/white/red AFV sign on this tank with that of the Royal Scots Greys' tank also shown in this book (see page 78). The Greys were also in Italy at this time and they too used names beginning with 'R' for some of their tanks. (I.W.M.)

36. *Filibuster*, a Matilda belonging to 'F' Squadron, 49th Battalion, Royal Tank Regiment, in the United Kingdom in 1942. The other squadrons in the battalion were 'G' and 'H', but the tactical signs used were those for 'A', 'B' and 'C' Squadrons in other regiments. (Keystone)

37. *Talisman*, a Churchill of 3rd Troop, 'A' Squadron, 48th Battalion, R.T.R., taking part in a tank landing exercise in 1942. The name can be seen above the gap in the hull side where the air-intake cover has been removed. Note the white bar under the unit code sign 175 to denote Army troops. (I.W.M.)

▲38 ▼39

26

1st Battalion Royal Tank Regiment, June 1944						Table 2

Reconnaissance Troop W. D. Numbers:
Stuarts (un-named): T.156480; T.236296; T.231209; T.231170; T.231239; T.236866; T.231213; T.156449; T.231154; T.156478.
Scout Cars, Humber (un-named): F.196435; F.196461; F.196453; F.196462.

'A' Squadron	W.D. No. T:	'B' Squadron	W.D. No. T:	'C' Squadron	W.D. No. T:
Sqn. HQ		Sqn. HQ		Sqn. HQ	
Anwenoit	189689	Miss Blandish II	190057	The Old Firm	189517
Anwecandoit	120486	Bertrand du Guesclin	190053	Tobruck Boy	190052
Ansodowe	190054	Bounaparte (sic)	120482	Champ II	120480
No. 1 Troop		No. 1 Troop		No. 1 Troop	
Ajax	189865	Cor Wullie	121747	–	121748
Black Sapper	187831	Atalanta	190064	–	189872
Anson	189522	Lili Marlene	190025	'19'	190024
Ark Royal	228502	Wherezatiger	212256	Sidi Rezegh II	212263
No. 2 Troop		No. 2 Troop		No. 2 Troop	
Annous	189557	Lady Godvia	121750	Fuka Walat	121743
Apache	189521	The Saint	189539	Cumon Thith Way	189879
The Herd of Asgaard	189812	Fair Maid o' Perth	121745	Farleesh	190022
Achtung	148512	Defiant	228675	Iz a Comin	148641
No. 3 Troop		No. 3 Troop		No. 3 Troop	
Angel	190032	El Abusiesse V	189530	Slaphappy	121742
Astrid	121740	Little Audrey II	189873	Miss–Kwoise	190026
Antoinette	189560	Betty Boop I	189524	G.U.T.S.	187826
Andromeda	212699	Jeanne D'Arc	228614	Donkey's Serenade	211909
No. 4 Troop		No. 4 Troop		No. 4 Troop	
Andrea	121746	Minerva	189531	Crippen I	189859
Again	190027	Diana	190031	Lord Crump III	189875
Ali Baba	189559	Venus	189867	Avenger II	190028
Ann	228542	Juno	228639	Adaptable VIII	211935

The tanks in the three fighting squadrons were Cromwells except for the fourth tank in each troop which was a Sherman 17pdr.

▼40

38. A group of Churchill IIIs of 'C' Squadron, 51st Battalion, Royal Tank Regiment on a training exercise in 1942, before leaving the United Kingdom for the Tunisian campaign. The three nearest tanks are *Centaur*, *Centurion* and *Cyclops*. (I.W.M.)

39. *Achilles*, *Apollo* and other Churchill tanks of 'A' Squadron, 51st Battalion, Royal Tank Regiment, in action near the Gothic Line in Italy. (I.W.M.)

40. 11th Hussars Daimler armoured cars in Tunis. This regiment did not use names for its AFVs, but the unit code number 76 can be seen below the jerboa sign. (I.W.M.)

random, although possibly in associated groups at troop level.

51st Battalion: The four Regimental HQ tanks were named after the Duke of Marlborough's four great battles: *Blenheim* (C.O.), *Oudenarde*, *Malplaquet* and *Ramilles*. In 'A' Squadron, names began with the letter 'A'; examples are *Adventurer*, *Audacious* and *Arrogant* (5th Troop). 'B' Squadron used names of British warships—*Malaya*, *Barham*, *Exeter* and *Severn*; and 'C' Squadron used names beginning with 'C'. When a Reconnaissance Troop of light tanks was added, these were named after Red Indian tribes such as *Blackfoot* and *Athabaska*.

As mentioned above, during the Second World War the 1st Battalion Royal Tank Regiment abandoned the system of allocating 'A' names to all tanks of the unit although some of the old names were retained for 'A' Squadron. Apart from these, a very miscellaneous collection of names, some very facetious, was adopted (and not infrequently changed) in the later years of the War—a list of those in use in June 1944 is appended in Table 2. (Note that the Reconnaissance Troop tanks and scout cars were un-named. Also, although the Regimental HQ tanks and the six anti-aircraft tanks of the AA Troop do appear to have been named, they have not been recorded (apart from *Skyraker*, a Crusader AA tank). However, Regimental HQ Comet tanks *Iron Duke IV* and *Long John Silver III* were in Berlin in 1945, and it is probable that these names were handed on from R.HQ tanks used in 1944.

4. Cavalry Regiments

There was far less consistency in the naming of armoured fighting vehicles in the mechanized cavalry regiments. In several regiments there is no evidence that names were ever given, and in others names only appear to have been used spasmodically. Where names were used, subjects like hunting, steeplechasing and flat racing were popular. The position is illustrated by the first two cavalry regiments to be mechanized, in 1928, as armoured car regiments: the 11th Hussars and the 12th Royal Lancers. The former appear never to have named their armoured vehicles (possibly the only exception was a Daimler armoured car briefly named *Amazon* before the name was ordered to be removed), whereas the latter named their armoured cars from the early days; examples are *Arethusa* and *Agamemnon*, which were Lanchesters in about 1935. Names in the 12th Lancers were generally given in accordance with the squadron letter—examples of Morris Armoured Reconnaissance Cars, 1939-40, were *Amberware*, *Arravale* ('A'

▲41 ▼42

Squadron); and *Cowes* and *Clyde* ('C' Squadron). Humber armoured cars in the Desert were also named, and the same general system seems to have been in operation when the Regiment was in Malaya in 1954. The following notes do not include all cavalry regiments that named their AFVs, but only those for which some evidence of the system used is available.

2nd Household Cavalry Regiment: When this unit was the armoured car regiment of the Guards Armoured Division, Regimental HQ used names beginning with 'H' (these included *Hercules* (C.O.), *Hengist* and *Horsa*). The Squadrons ('A'—'D') adopted AFV names commencing with the Squadron letter; random examples are *Argo, Beaufort, Bull, Crusader, Caesar, Dipper*, and *Diver*. Most of the names were of former chargers or drum horses of the Household Cavalry, racehorses or hunts.

Household Cavalry Training Regiment: Armoured cars and scout cars were all named after racehorses; examples are *Portcullis, Kings Arms, Windsor Lad, Seven Dials, Brown Jack*, and *Sir Troops*.

1st King's Dragoon Guards: During the early stages of the Second World War the armoured cars in this Regiment bore the names of their drivers' home towns; examples are *Liverpool* and *Stamford*, both of which were Marmon-Herrington

41. A Morris reconnaissance armoured car of 'C' Squadron, 12th Royal Lancers, in France in 1940. The car's name (*Cowes*) is displayed on the side of the hull, and the unit code number 129 is in white on a black rectangle with the white bar denoting Army troops. The camouflage colours are probably middle bronze-green and deep bronze-green. (I.W.M.)

42. A prisoner running past Daimler armoured car *Beaufort* of 'B' Squadron, 2nd Household Cavalry Regiment, in Normandy. At this time the Regiment was Corps troops of 8 Corps, whose sign appears below the W.D. number on the rear plate. (I.W.M.)

43. *Hercules*, the C.O.'s Staghound armoured car of the 2nd Household Cavalry Regiment, entering Brussels. The name and W.D. number appear near the bottom of the glacis plate. (I.W.M.)

44. Daimler armoured cars of the Household Cavalry Training Regiment lined up for firing practice. The nearest car is *Jack Horner* and the third one is *Brown Jack*.

45. Grants of the 3rd Carabiniers in action in Burma in 1945. The name *Angel* can be seen on the side door of the tank in the foreground. (I.W.M.)

▲43

▲44 ▼45

armoured cars in action at Tobruk. By 1944 there is some evidence that names following squadron letters were in use.

The Queen's Bays, 9th Queen's Royal Lancers and 10th Royal Hussars: These Regiments, which formed the 2nd Armoured Brigade for the greater part of the Second World War, seem only in 1940 to have used tank names with any degree of consistency. The Bays used an assortment of names including those of racehorses such as *Miss Mowbray* ('A' Squadron) and *Empire Pride* ('C' Squadron). The 9th Lancers apparently used names following the squadron letter, an example being *Victorious*, which was a Regimental HQ Covenanter in 1941. The 10th Royal Hussars followed a system similar to that adopted by the 9th Lancers, possibly over a longer period; an example is *Hornblower*, which was a Reconnaissance Troop Stuart in Italy.

The 3rd Carabiniers: This Regiment used tank names from the time it was first mechanized in India; *Achilles, Adonis* and *Cricklade* were names borne by Mark VI light tanks in 1940. It was also about this time that the Carabiniers' feathers badge was painted on the turrets. By the spring of 1942, Regimental HQ (equipped with carriers) used the names of Surtees' 'Handley Cross' characters (*Binjimin, Mr. Sponge* and *Belinda* for example) for HQ Squadron; hounds' names (*Arden, Bellman* and *Dauntless*) for the Scout Troop; and race meetings (*Aintree, Punchestown* and *Lingfield*) for the Mortar Troop. In the Burma campaign, the Lee and Grant tanks used had names beginning with the Squadron letter; *Auk* and *Angel* are examples. (The name *Aintree*, mentioned above, was revived after the War for an M-10 SP 17 pdr. of 'A' Squadron in 1953.)

4th/7th Royal Dragoon Guards: Naming systems in this Regiment varied during the War years, until by 1945 tanks were named solely at the discretion of their commanders. In France during 1940 'A' Squadron Mark VIB light tanks were named after steeplechasers (*Airgead Sios, Ally Sloper, Eclipse* and *Drogheda*); and 'B' and 'C' Squadrons took their names from hunts (*Belvoir* and *Cotswold*). By the end of 1941, 'A' Squadron (at this time equipped with Covenanters) was using the names of towns—a system that was continued until after the Normandy landings—including *Bath, Hereford* and *Exeter*. Regimental Headquarters' armoured fighting vehicles took the names of the Regiment's battle honours. Names given to some of the Daimler scout cars were *Oudenarde, Malplaquet* and *Ypres*; and names used for Covenanters included *Dettingen* and *Balaclava*.

▲46 ▼47

46. 4th/7th Royal Dragoon Guards' Mark VIB
light tanks in France, 1940; on the left is
Drogheda and the other is *Airgead Sios*. Note
the very prominent white square on the hull sides
and front, used as an AFV recognition mark at
this time. The 4th/7th R.D.G. were the Divisional
Cavalry Regiment for the 2nd Infantry Division.
The 'A' Squadron tactical sign triangle was red
whereas later it would have been white for
unbrigaded troops. (I.W.M.)

47. Daimler armoured cars of 1st King's Dragoon
Guards entering the Sicilian town of Trani in
September 1943. This Regiment is not known to
have used names for its AFVs but did sometimes
paint on its Regimental eagle badge as can be
seen in this photograph. According to the
Regimental history vehicles were painted green
and brown before leaving North Africa. (I.W.M.)

48. 1st King's Dragoon Guards en route to
Denmark in May 1945 passing a column of
German soldiers. This AEC armoured car has
The Royals eagle badge over the 12 Corps
sign. (I.W.M.)

49. A knocked-out Stuart of The Royal Scots
Greys in Tunisia. This turretless tank, *Astra III*,
belonged to Regimental HQ—probably the
Reconnaissance Troop. (I.W.M.)

▲48 ▼49

5th Royal Iniskilling Dragoon Guards: In 1940 (when this Regiment was equipped with Mark VIB light tanks and scout carriers) Regimental HQ armoured fighting vehicles names began with the letter 'H'; the tanks *Hengist* and *Horsa* are examples. This being the case, it is possible that the other vehicles also used their squadron letter. Even fewer details are available for later periods, but it is known that the Centurians of the Regiment were named when operating in Korea.

Royal Scots Greys: No obvious system was employed and names were not consistently used. Names borne by Shermans during the early part of the Italian campaign included *Sheik* ('A' Squadron), *Bramham Moor* ('B' Squadron), *Repulse* and *Renown* (both British warship names used by 'C' Squadron). Also at this time the Regiment displayed a Scottish thistle on the fronts of its tanks.

3rd The King's Own Hussars: This Regiment seems to have stuck fairly consistently to names following the squadron letter, although otherwise varied. Regimental HQ tanks took the names of battle honours, the C.O.'s being *Moodkee*. Others were *Dettingen, Salamanca* and *Sabraon*.

4th Queen's Own Hussars: No discernible pattern of names used by the armoured fighting vehicles of this Regiment has been discovered. The only example we have is *Dauntless*, which was the Commanding Officer's Sherman command tank (with a dummy gun) from about September 1943 through the Italian campaign to 1945.

7th Queen's Own Hussars: All that is known of the naming system used by this Regiment (which saw action in the Western Desert, Burma and Italy) is that tanks, when named, were given ones that began with the squadron letter.

8th King's Royal Irish Hussars: The following naming system was first used with the Regiment's Stuart light tanks in the Western Desert, and remained throughout the War, and during the Korean campaign. Regimental HQ used racehorse names beginning with the letter 'H'; the C.O.'s was named *Hurry on*, after the celebrated sire of three Derby winners. 'A' Squadron gave racehorse (flat race) names, but beginning with the letter 'A'; examples are *Abbot of Chantry* and *Allandale*, the respective names given to a Cromwell and a Challenger tank in 1945. 'B' Squadron gave the names of hounds beginning with the letter 'B'; examples are *Boxer* and *Bellman*. 'C' Squadron allotted the names of racehorses beginning with the letter 'C'; examples are *Captain Cuttle, Coronach* and *Call Boy* (the famous trio of Derby winners mentioned above).

13th/18th Royal Hussars: AFV names do

▲50 ▼51

50. *Renown*, a Sherman of 15th Troop, 'C' Squadron, Royal Scots Greys, negotiating an obstacle during the Italian campaign in 1943. Traces of the unusual spotted camouflage system added in Sicily appear to have been left towards the rear of the hull and turret. It was also at about this time that some of the Grey's tanks carried a thistle insignia on the hull front. (I.W.M.)

51. A desolate-looking Stuart tank of 'B' Squadron, 8th King's Royal Irish Hussars, after it had been knocked-out in the Desert in December, 1941. The vehicle's name (*Bellman*) and the white/red/white recognition signs are prominent, as are the 4th Armoured Brigade sign and (faintly) the W.D. number T 28037 in white.

52. Shermans of the 3rd The King's Own Hussars being reviewed in Syria in 1943. The nearest tank is *Argosy* of 'A' Squadron—slightly above the name can be seen the New Zealand fern leaf emblem awarded to the 9th Armoured Brigade for their co-operation with the New Zealanders in the Desert battles. The 9th Armoured Brigade sign combined with the unit sign (the number 40 on a red rectangle) shown on the upper left side of the glacis plate has been scratched out by the censor. (I.W.M.)

53. Cromwell tanks of 8th King's Royal Irish Hussars, the Armoured Reconnaissance Regiment of the 7th Armoured Division, well turned out for a victory parade in Germany, 1945. The fact that the prefix to the W.D. numbers has been omitted is a little unusual, but the white tactical signs that were so unpopular in action are correct. (I.W.M.)

not appear to have been used for the Regiment's light tanks, but by 1944 (when equipped with Shermans) the common system of names following the squadron letter was employed for 'A', 'B' and 'C' Squadrons. This Regiment, which by D-Day was in the 27th Armoured Brigade, carried large identification numbers usually on the turrets. These numbers were: 22-36 inclusive ('A' Squadron); 44-58 inclusive ('B' Squadron), examples are *Boleyn* 47, *Borgia* 48 and *Boadicea* 49; and 66-80 inclusive ('C' Squadron). Regimental HQ used numbers below 20; examples are *Balaclava* 10 and *Twelfth Knight* 12. The numbers were probably in red with a white outline; and the names were in white on small black panels on the hull sides, with a small, geometrical, squadron tactical sign just behind them.

14th/20th Hussars: When first mechanized in India in 1939, this Regiment carried its black hawk badge on the turret sides of its light tanks. In about 1940 the four Regimental HQ tanks bore the names of British Castles such as *Edinburgh* and the C.O.'s tank, *Windsor Castle*. Three of R.HQ's Universal Carriers —*Cholmondeley*, *Marjoriebanks* and *Featherstonehaugh*—were named by the Intelligence Officer. 'A' Squadron tanks took their names from Regimental battle honours; 'B' Squadron's were named after Derby winners; and 'C' Squadron adopted British naval names. In 1942 the Regiment was serving with the 31st Indian Armoured Division in Iraq, and the following are examples of names used during this period: *Iron Duke* and *Sturdee* were Mark VIB light tanks of 'C' Squadron; and *D'Artagnan*, *Athos* and *Ringer* (India Pattern wheeled carriers used by the Reconnaissance Troop). However, from 1943 onwards, names for AFVs do not appear to have been used.

15th/19th The King's Royal Hussars: The light tanks and scout carriers used by this Regiment on its first campaign in France prior to Dunkirk, were allotted names in accordance with the squadron letter. This naming system was adopted until the end of the Regiment's Normandy operations, after which AFVs were rarely named. Examples are *Appollo* (sic), *Ajax* and *Achilles* (Covenanters of 1st Troop, 'A' Squadron in 1942); *Apollo*, *Achilles* and *Adonais* (sic) (Cromwells used by 5th Troop in 1943); and *Revenge* (a Daimler scout car of either Regimental HQ or the Reconnaissance Troop).

16th/5th Lancers: From 1940 until near the end of the War this Regiment was brigaded with the 17th/21st Lancers, the 2nd Lothians and the Border Horse in the 26th Armoured Brigade (6th Armoured

▲54

▲55 ▼56

54. *Blenheim*—the name is partly visible below the smoke discharger—a Mark VIC light tank of 'B' Squadron, 10th Royal Hussars, after it had been knocked-out and burnt in France, 1940. (I.W.M.)

55. 'Music while you work' for men of the 13th/18th Royal Hussars working on their Shermans shortly before D-Day, 1944. The nearest tank is *Charmer* and the other is *Conquest*, which has the turret number 66 although it is not evident in this photograph. The names are positioned above the appliqué armour on the hull sides. On the nose plates, from left to right, are the bridge group number 30, the unit code 51 and the 27th Armoured Brigade sign, which has been carefully deleted by the censor. (I.W.M.)

56. *Sturdee*, a Mark VI (India Pattern) light tank of 'C' Squadron, 14th/20th Hussars, providing a focal point for some passing natives in Persia, 1941. Note the Government of India broad arrow and registration number on the nose plate. (I.W.M.)

57. The Sherman tank *Balaclava*, of Regimental HQ, 13th/18th Royal Hussars, rooting out enemy troops positioned behind crashed Allied gliders in Normandy, 1944. The Regimental number 10 is shown on the turret, and the name, which is not visible, is on the hull side; the unit code 51 is on the left rear and the 27th Armoured Brigade sign is on the right—but deleted by the censor. (I.W.M.)

▲58 ▼59

Division). In 1941 the 16th/5th Lancers used the names of Derby winners for tanks in 'A' Squadron; some examples are *Minoru, Manna, Hyperion, Hermit, Coronach, Call Boy, Blenheim* and *Blue Peter*—early in 1943 these were changed to *Uncle Tom Cobley* and his associates, including the *Grey Mare*. Various names were used by 'B' and 'C' Squadrons, but Valentine tanks of Regimental HQ in 1941 were named after castles: *Barnard Castle, Dover Castle* and *Arundel Castle*. (There was also a scout car named *Porcupine*.)

17th/21st Lancers: First equipped with light tanks in India in 1938, this Regiment was back in the United Kingdom by 1941, but this time equipped with Valentines. Regimental HQ tanks were named after racehorses such as *Grand Chance* and *Saint Simon*. 'A', 'B' and 'C' Squadrons also favoured racehorse names, but they all followed the Squadron letter; examples are *Ali Baba, April the Fifth, Bogskar, Blue Peter* and *Cameronian*.

22nd Dragoons: This new, mechanized cavalry Regiment was raised in 1940, but it was not until the receipt of Covenanters in 1942 that they began naming their tanks. Regimental HQs four tanks were named after the British patron saints *St. George, St. Andrews, St. Patrick* and *St. David*. 'A' Squadron used the names of towns; 'B' Squadron adopted battle names; and 'C' Squadron chose aircraft names. The troops used an alphabetical sequence—*Thunderbolt, Tornado* and *Typhoon*—and this system appears to have been continued, to some extent, after the Regiment was equipped with Sherman Crab flail tanks. *Stirling IV* was a 'C' Squadron Sherman command battle tank at this time. Exceptions were the Sherman battle tanks of 'A' Squadron's HQ Troop; examples of names used by them in 1944 are *Ajax, Achilles* and *Leander*.

23rd Hussars: Few details are available, but it is known that by 1944 the Reconnaissance Troop (equipped with Stuart light tanks) were using names including *Grind, Grumble* and *Grunt*. 'C' Squadron (Shermans) had tanks named after cities, such as *City of Liverpool*.

24th Lancers: This Regiment was raised during the Second World War and served in the 8th Armoured Brigade on D-Day. It used the common system of names following the squadron letter—these were diagonally painted in script across the nose plates of the Regiment's Sherman tanks.

25th Dragoons: The 3rd Carabiniers raised this Regiment in India, and little is known of the naming system employed by them. The only information available is that two of the Regiment's Lee tanks in Burma were named *Surrey* and *Shrewsbury*.

27th Lancers: An armoured car Regiment,

58. Lined up and ready for inspection—Covenanters of the 15th/19th The King's Royal Hussars in England in 1941. The nearest tanks are *Achilles* and *Apollo* of 'A' Squadron. The camouflage colours are khaki-brown with very dark brown disruptive patches. (I.W.M.)

59. *Barnard Castle*, a Valentine of Regimental HQ, 16th/5th Lancers with the 6th Armoured Division, being reviewed by King George VI in 1941. (Central Press)

60. A close-support Matilda (*Bendigo*) of 'C' Squadron HQ, 17th/21st Lancers, towing a Valentine (*Bedale*, of 4th Troop, 'B' Squadron) out of trouble. The chalked crosses on or near the tactical signs are temporary markings for the exercise in the United Kingdom in which these tanks were taking part in 1941. (Assoc. Press)

61. Sherman tank *Armageddon* of 'A' Squadron, 24th Lancers, on a D-Day beach in 1944. The name is in script in the centre of the nose plate, and to the right is the (censored) unit code sign 995 in white on a red rectangle combined with the 8th Armoured Brigade badge. (I.W.M.)

▲60 ▼61

62. Self-propelled 75mm half-tracks of 27th Lancers, an armoured car regiment, firing against enemy positions in Italy. The vehicle farthest from the camera is *Acorn Inn* of 'A' Squadron. (I.W.M.)

63. Men of the 1st East Riding Yeomanry having a little light relief from working on their Shermans shortly before D-Day. Small 'C' Squadron tactical signs can be seen on the nearest tank, *Casus Belli*, in the middle of the hull side and the middle of the nose plate immediately above the unit code number (53). Note the mobilization number and L.C.T. number below the co-driver's hatch. (I.W.M.)

64. *Cornwall*, a Covenanter III with an unusual name for a Scottish regiment (1st Fife and Forfar), being inspected by foreign visitors during a

9th Armoured Division exercise in the United Kingdom in 1942. (I.W.M.)

65. *Golden Eye*, a Mark VIB light tank belonging to the 2nd Troop of 'C' Squadron, 2nd Fife and Forfar Yeomanry, on manoeuvres in Northern Ireland, 1941. The name is positioned on the left-hand side just above the bridge group number. (I.W.M.)

66. Infantry of the Hertfordshire Regiment take cover behind the bank of the River Elbe, while a Comet of 'B' Squadron, 2nd Fife and Forfar Yeomanry, prepares for action, 1945. The name *Why Worry* is displayed next to the hull machine-gun, and the unit code sign (53), the W.D. number and 11th Armoured Division sign all appear faintly on the nose plate. (I.W.M.)

▲62 ▼63

38

raised by the 12th Royal Lancers, whose AFV names began with the squadron letter. *Demon, Dragon, Dominie* and *Dopey* are examples of the names given to scout cars and armoured cars of 5th Troop, 'D' Squadron, in about 1941. Another example is *Acorn Inn* which was an SP 75mm half-track of 'A' Squadron's support troop (7th Troop) and was used in Italy in 1945.

5. Yeomanry Regiments

These Territorial cavalry regiments converted to armour, and for which AFV names are known, are given below in alphabetical order rather than in order of seniority.

1st East Riding Yeomanry: This Regiment appears to have mainly used the system of names following the squadron letter; examples for 'C' Squadron range from Beaverette light armoured cars in late 1940 to Shermans in 1944. 'B' Squadron also seems to have adopted this system. However, there were exceptions to the rule: an 'A' Squadron HQ Sherman tank named *St. George*, which also bore the large Regimental number 2; and a 'C' Squadron Mark VIB light tank in February 1940 named *Quidnunc*.

1st Fife and Forfar Yeomanry: Some Mark VIB light tanks used by this Regiment in France between 1939 and 1940 bore the names of animals, such as *Puma, Panda* and *Terrier*. After this period no obvious system is apparent, except that 'B' and 'C' Squadrons may have had names beginning with the squadron letter. A Regimental HQ Covenanter was named *Revenge*.

2nd Fife and Forfar Yeomanry: Light tanks of 'C' Squadron in Northern Ireland in 1941 were named after birds, but by the end of the War this system had changed. The Regiment was by this time equipped with Comet tanks and these took their names from battles. 'B' Squadron adopted the names of racehorses—*Brown Jack* and *Why Worry*; 'A' Squadron used the names of constellations; and the Regimental HQ tanks were named *St. George, St. Andrew, St. Patrick* and *St. David*.

1st Royal Gloucestershire Hussars: The three 'sabre' Squadrons of this Regiment, 'A', 'B' and 'D', as well as Regimental HQ, used local place-names for their Valentine tanks between 1941 and 1942; examples are, *Leighterton* (R.HQ), *The Royal William* and *Avening* ('A' Squadron); *Perrott's Brook* ('B' Squadron); *Didmarton, Tockington* and *Winterbourne* ('D' Squadron).

2nd Royal Gloucestershire Hussars: There is some reason to believe that the tanks of this Regiment, when names were used, were named to follow the Squadron letters: 'F', 'G' and 'H'. Two of the light tanks of 'H' Squadron in 1940 were

▲64

▲65 ▼66

▲67 ▼68

67. 20th Armoured Brigade (Independent) on an exercise in England, 1942. The tank is a Valentine, *Tockington*, of 'D' Squadron, 1st Royal Gloucestershire Hussars. The name is painted and outlined and appears above the driver's visor.

68. *Hood*, a Mark VIB of 2nd Troop, 'H' Squadron (the equivalent of 'C' Squadron in other regiments), 2nd Royal Gloucestershire Hussars. (I.W.M.)

69. A Daimler armoured car and two Humber Mark IIIs belonging to the Inns of Court Regiment (an armoured car regiment) on Exercise Spartan in 1943. The nearest car is *Questing Beast* and the other Humber is *Rough Justice*, both of 'B' Squadron. (I.W.M.)

70. 3rd County of London Yeomanry taking part in an exercise in England, 1941. The Mark VIB light tank is *Athos* of 'A' Squadron, but the scout car belongs to Headquarters, 22nd Armoured Brigade of the 1st Armoured Division. (I.W.M.)

71. A line-up of Shermans of the 3rd County of London Yeomanry in Sicily in 1943. *Abdiel* is nearest, then comes *Aphrodite*; note the unit serial number 6 on the turret bin of the former. (Details of the numbers used by this Regiment are given in the text, page 41.) (The Sharpshooters—Boris Mollo)

Hadrian and *Hood*. (The geometric tactical signs used were identical to those used for 'A', 'B' and 'C' Squadrons in other regiments.)

Inns of Court Regiment: Originally an officer-producing unit only, this Regiment was turned into an armoured car regiment and allotted to the 9th Armoured Division early in 1941. *Rough Justice* and *Questing Beast* were names used for 'B' Squadron's Humber Armoured Cars in 1943. It is not known whether names were still used in the north-west Europe campaign when the Regiment was a Corps armoured car regiment.

3rd County of London Yeomanry: Tank names following the squadron letter were used by this Regiment through the greater part of the War; examples are *Ant*, *Antelope* and *Asp*, which were Mark VIB light tanks of 1st Troop, 'A' Squadron, in about 1940. At the end of the War, two of Regimental HQ's tanks were named *Sharpshooter* (taken from the Regiment's nickname) and *Jerboa*. During the Regiment's time in Italy and Sicily a numbering system devised by the Technical Adjutant (Mr. D. H. Jackson, who has kindly supplied the details) was used as a quick means of accounting for the AFVs in the unit. No tank commander wanted the number 1 (because of its target significance to the enemy), therefore the numbering system started at number 5. The numbers were shown, on Sherman tanks, on the sides of the turret bins and were allotted as follows: 'A' Squadron, 5 upwards; 'B' Squadron, 21 upwards; and 'C' Squadron, 37 upwards. The R.HQ tanks were numbered 61-64 and the scout cars 1-10, therefore duplicating some of the tanks' numbers.

1st Lothians and Border Horse: Few details of this Regiment in 1940 are available, but by 1944 when it was equipped with Sherman Crab flail tanks, the squadrons were using various naming systems. 'A' Squadron adopted the names of famous Scots (*Colin Campbell, Rob Roy* and *William Wallace*); 'B' Squadron used the names of Scottish castles and districts (*Craigmillar, Tantallon, Dunbar* and *Gallowgate, Sauchiehall* and *Canongate*); and 'C' Squadron used the names of such diverse characters as *Constable of Chester* (a Sherman battle tank) and *Wandering Willie*.

2nd Lothians and Border Horse: This Regiment was in the 26th Armoured Brigade in 1941, and the Valentine tanks used bore the names of Scottish places following the squadron letter. Examples for 'A' Squadron are *Armadale* and a Matilda close-support tank which used the nickname for Edinburgh, *Auld Reekie*; and names used by 'C' Squadron included *Chirnside* and *Craiglochart*.

▲69

▲70 ▼71

▲72 ▼73

1st Northamptonshire Yeomanry: It was not until this Regiment was using Sherman tanks, with which it fought in north-west Europe, that tank names appear to have been adopted. 'C' Squadron used Northants place-names and it may well have been that the other squadrons followed suit. However, we do know of one 'B' Squadron tank named *Indiana*—which is a long way from Northamptonshire.

North Irish Horse: This Regiment (which was actually classed as militia cavalry rather than yeomanry) was equipped first with Valentines and then Churchills both in the United Kingdom and in action in Italy. Churchill tanks with 'A', 'B' and 'C' Squadrons were given those names of counties and towns in Northern Ireland which corresponded to the squadron letter such as *Ardess, Blackrock* and *Castlerobin*. The letters 'D', 'E' and 'F' were allotted to Regimental HQ, the Reconnaissance Troop (an example of which is *Enniskillen*, a Sherman used in Italy) and spare tanks.

Sherwood Rangers Yeomanry (*Nottinghamshire Yeomanry*): At the beginning of the Second World War this Regiment was an unmechanized cavalry unit, and it was not until the end of 1941 that it was equipped with tanks. A year later, in the Western Desert, the Regimental HQ tanks were very appropriately named *Robin Hood, Little John, Friar Tuck* (all Grants) and *Maid Marion* (a Crusader). The name *Robin Hood* was perpetuated in a R.HQ Sherman until 1945. The other tanks in the

▲74

▲75 ▼76

72. This close-up of *Mellerstang*, a Sherman Crab flail tank of the 1st Lothians and Border Horse, seen here in Normandy in 1944, gives a good view of the .5 Browning heavy machine-gun as well as the regimental tank number 60. (I.W.M.)

73. *Currie*, a Valentine of 4th Troop, 'C' Squadron, 2nd Lothians and Border Horse, on an exercise with the 6th Armoured Division in 1941. Note that the formation sign is outlined in white and that a coloured patch appears in the lower half, a device which took the place of unit code numbers in this Division.

74. *Castlederg*, a Churchill of the North Irish Horse, providing cover for infantrymen in Italy. The name appears very faintly at the bottom of the engine air-intake on the hull side. The plate on the rear of the turret seems to indicate that the vehicle belongs to the 3rd Troop of 'C' Squadron. (I.W.M.)

75. Men of the 1st Northamptonshire Yeomanry taking a break from hostilities in Normandy, 1944. The 'C' Squadron Sherman behind them has the name *Helmdon* (a Northants village) exactly above the front appliqué armour. (I.W.M.)

76. Regimental Headquarters of the Sherwood Rangers Yeomanry in the Desert in 1942. The C.O.'s Grant, *Robin Hood II*, is in the foreground with a 'B' Squadron tank behind it.

▲77

▲78 ▼79

Regiment may not have been named at this time, but in 1944 the Shermans of 'A', 'B' and 'C' Squadrons in Normandy appear to have had names following the squadron letter. 'A' Squadron at any rate had tanks named *Aberdeen, Akilla* and *Achilles*; and 'C' Squadron had a Sherman DD (Duplex Drive—both 'B' and 'C' Squadrons were equipped with these for the D-Day landings) named *Bardin Collos* (probably, like *Akilla*, derived from an Egyptian expression).

Staffordshire Yeomanry: This Regiment began the War as horsed cavalry, and was first fully equipped with tanks in the Western Desert in August 1942. Names beginning with the squadron letter were used by 'B' Squadron's Grants—*Battle-axe, Battlespite, Blenheim* and *Battleship* (a Lee). The C.O.'s Grant at Regimental HQ was named *Defiance*, and was the only tank of the Regiment to survive the Battle of Alamein. In Normandy in 1944, the Regiment appears to have been using the same system, as the following names given to 'A' Squadron's Shermans show: *Accuser, Avenger* and *Agressor* (sic). One of the R.HQ's Anti-Aircraft Troops Crusader AA IIIs was named *Chaos*.

Warwickshire Yeomanry: Another Territorial cavalry unit mechanized after the outbreak of War, the Warwickshire Yeomanry completed its re-equipment not long before the Battle of Alamein in October 1942. 'A' Squadron was equipped with Crusaders and 'B' and 'C' Squadrons with American Shermans and Grants. 'B' Squadron used the names of American states and cities for their tanks, a practice continued into the Italian campaign when the whole Regiment had Shermans. 'C' Squadron apparently used the names of Warwickshire places—4th Troop of 'C' Squadron in Italy being *Compton Verney, Compton Wynyates* and *Compton*

Scorpion (Shermans).

Royal Wiltshire Yeomanry: The history of this Regiment during the Second World War paralleled that of the Warwickshire Yeomanry when both were in the 9th Armoured Brigade. It was first fully equipped with tanks for the Battle of El Alamein in October 1942. The Regiment used the names of Wiltshire towns, villages and pubs for its tanks; these were shown in large yellow letters on the hull sides. The C.O.'s Grant tank (later a Sherman) of Regimental HQ was named *Trowbridge* (the peace-time headquarters of the unit). *Salisbury*, *Devizes* and *Cricklade* were names given respectively to tanks of 'A', 'B' and 'C' Squadrons. Three public houses commemorated by 'A' Squadron were *Old Bell*, *Bath Arms* and *Rose and Crown*.

6. Infantry Battalions converted to armour

As a result of the decision to expand Britain's armoured forces following the fall of France in 1940, many infantry battalions were converted to armour. The majority of these were intended as army tank battalions in close support of the infantry, but two armoured divisions—the Guards and the 42nd—were also formed from infantry. After conversion, the

77. *Akilla*, a Sherman of 'A' Squadron, Sherwood Rangers Yeomanry, and its crew in Normandy. (I.W.M.)

78. *Battleaxe*, a Grant of the Staffordshire Yeomanry, passing through Tarhuna after the Battle of El Alamein in 1942. This 'B' Squadron tank has its name in small letters on the side of the 75mm gun sponson as well as in much larger roughly painted letters on the hull side; the latter may have been added for tactical purposes. (I.W.M.)

79. Crusader AA III tank *Chaos* of the Staffordshire Yeomanry. The vehicle's name is faint but can be seen just above the gap between the boxes stowed on the glacis plate, to its right is the 27th Armoured Brigade sign. (I.W.M.)

80. *Chicago*, a Grant of the Warwickshire Yeomanry in the Desert in 1942. The camouflage is sand colour with dark grey disruptive patches —note how one of these is intended to break-up the sharp outline of the front of the upper hull. (Yeoman Yeoman—Warwickshire Yeomanry History)

81. Sherman tanks of the Warwickshire Yeomanry lined up for a parade in Syria in 1943. The nearest tank is *Minnesota* of 1st Troop, 'B' Squadron. Note that the censor has deleted the New Zealand fern leaf emblem (under the 'E' in Minnesota) from the hull side. (I.W.M.)

82. The Commanding Officer of the Royal Wiltshire Yeomanry leading a parade in his Sherman *Trowbridge*—Syria, 1943. The name and tactical signs were in yellow, and the New Zealand fern appears above the 'B' of Trowbridge. (The Royal Wiltshire Yeomanry—J. R. I. Platt)

▲80

▲81 ▼82

83. The Sherman command tank of the C.O. of 1st (Armoured) Coldstream Guards in late 1944. This vehicle is named *Monck*, after one of the Commanding Officer's distinguished predecessors. (I.W.M.)

84. A Cromwell of the 2nd Armoured Welsh Guards, the Armoured Reconnaissance Regiment of the Guards Armoured Division, passing burning German transport on the road to Brussels in 1944. Although few details can be obtained some, at least, of the Welsh Guards' tanks appear to have been named. (I.W.M.)

83▶

▲85 ▼86

Guards' battalions retained their basic original titles, but the line regiments were renamed 'Regiments, Royal Armoured Corps'. These line regiments were numbered from 107 to 116 and from 141 to 163, although in some cases they were allowed to retain their original titles as subsidiary designations.

Guards Armoured Division: By 1942 the organization of the tank regiments consisted of the 2nd Armoured Grenadier Guards, the 1st Armoured Coldstream Guards and the 2nd Armoured Irish Guards in the 5th Guards Armoured Brigade. The 2nd Armoured Reconnaissance Welsh Guards were added in 1943. (Notes on some of these regiments will be found below.)

1st Armoured Coldstream Guards: The R.HQ tanks were named after famous colonels of the Regiment, such as *Monck* (the C.O.'s tank) and *Codrington*. The Technical Adjutant's Humber scout car, which is now in the Tank Museum at Bovington, was named *Jack in the Box II* (not a colonel of the Coldstream Guards!) Few details are available for No. 1 and 2 Squadrons, but it is known that No. 3 Squadron used the names of birds for its tanks; an example is 3rd Troop, which at some time had tanks named *Kestrel*, *Kite* and *Kingfisher*.

2nd Armoured Irish Guards: All three squadrons of this Battalion named their tanks after Irish place-names. No. 1 Squadron used names beginning with 'A' (*Ardnacrush* and *Ardmore*); No. 2 Squadron took names beginning with 'B' (*Black Sod* and *Bantry*) and No. 3 Squadron used names beginning with 'C' (*Clochan* and *Cloneen*). The C.O.'s tank was named *St. Patrick*, and the other three tanks of Battalion HQ were named *Ulster*, *Leinster* and *Connaught*.

6th Guards Tank Brigade: When it was originally the Second Armoured Brigade in the Guards Armoured Division this formation consisted of the 4th Armoured Grenadier Guards, the 3rd Armoured Scots Guards and the 2nd Armoured Welsh Guards. Later it became an independent tank brigade, and from early 1943 to the end of the War the Welsh Guards were replaced by the 4th Armoured Coldstream Guards.

4th Battalion Grenadier Guards: All the tanks employed by this Battalion in 1944 (which were Churchills, except for the Stuarts used by the Reconnaissance Troop) were named after English places. Those names adopted by Battalion HQ and the Reconnaissance Troop (including its scout cars) began with the letter 'W'. (The other scout cars were named after aircraft.) In No. 1 Squadron the troops used alphabetical sequences; Squadron HQ Troop used the letter 'D';

▲87 ▼88

85. Covenanters of the 2nd Armoured Irish Guards being inspected in the United Kingdom in 1942. Squadrons of this Regiment named their tanks after Irish towns and villages, and Battalion HQ used the names of Irish provinces such as *Ulster* (shown here). The bridge group sign 16 in black and yellow is clearly visible, although the Guards Armoured Division sign is hidden by the centre man. Note how the unit code sign 53 is repeated on the mens helmets. (I.W.M.)

86. A Churchill VI of 9th Troop, No. 2 Squadron, 4th Battalion Grenadier Guards, in about 1943. Although this Troop retained the names of towns beginning with 'H' for its AFVs the name *Hythe* disappeared later.

87. *Esk*, the Left Flank Squadron Leader's tank (a Churchill III) of the 3rd Battalion Scots Guards. This photograph was taken in 1943 when the 3rd Scots Guards were the second regiment (with yellow tactical signs) of the 6th Guards Tank Brigade: later it became the junior regiment in the Brigade.

88. Churchill tanks of 7th Troop (note the gun muzzle covers), 'B' Squadron, 107th Regiment, R.A.C., on a training exercise. One of these is *Bustler*, although the name is not visible. The bridge group sign, with the yellow ring blacked-out, and the unit code sign 157 can just be seen on the nose plate of the leading AFV. (I.W.M.)

and Troops 1-5 used 'A', 'B', 'C', 'E' and 'F' respectively. No. 2 Squadron HQ Troop used the letter 'N'; and Troops 6-10 were allotted the letters 'F', 'K', 'G', 'H' and 'Y' respectively. No. 3 Squadron HQ Troop used the letter 'M'; and Troops 11-15 used 'P', 'S', 'L', 'O' and 'T' respectively. It should be noted that occasionally the tanks' names were replaced by others—no doubt this coincided with a change of crew.

4th Battalion Coldstream Guards: The Battalion HQ's AFVs of this unit were named after birds; examples are *Eagle*, which was the C.O.'s Churchill tank; *Eaglet*, the C.O.'s scout car; and *Cuckoo*, a captured Panther tank attached to HQ. Some of the other names were also appropriately chosen; *Pigeon* and *Owlet* being, respectively, the Signals Officer's and Intelligence Officer's scout cars. No. 1 Squadron's tanks were all given the names of Coldstream Guards battle honours; Squadron HQ tanks were *Egypt, Barossa* and *Peninsula*. Troops 1-4 used the names of battles beginning with the letters 'A', 'M', 'S' and 'T' respectively; and No. 5 Troop contained tanks named *Nive, Waterloo* and *Gibraltar*. Names used by Troops 6-10 began with 'B', 'C', 'E', 'L' and 'P' respectively; and Troops 11-15 adopted names beginning with the letters 'B', 'D', 'M', 'T' and 'V' respectively. Animal and bird names were used by No. 2 Squadron, whose Squadron HQ used the names *Tiger, Jackal, Jaguar* and *Rook*. No. 3 Squadron adopted names of British warships; and names used by their Squadron HQ began with the letter 'R'.

3rd Battalion Scots Guards: All AFVs used Scottish place-names (mountains, lochs, towns, islands etc.) or Scottish characters, real or fictional, although names were changed from time to time. The full list for June 1944 is given in Table 3. The squadron titles were those traditional in the Scots Guards, but the tactical signs used were the same as those for R.HQ, 'A', 'B' and 'C' Squadrons in other regiments.

7. Infantry of the Line

107th Regiment, Royal Armoured Corps (King's Own): The C.O.'s tank is believed to have been named *Lion* (after the King's Own Royal Regiment's cap badge, the Lion of England); and the tanks in the three squadrons were given names following the squadron letters. In 'A' Squadron, the Churchills used by 5th Troop in 1944 consisted of *Avenger, Alert* and *Angler*.

110th Regiment, Royal Armoured Corps (Border): The AFVs, and many of the transport vehicles of this unit (converted from the 5th Battalion, The Border Regiment, in September 1941 and disbanded at the end of 1943) were given names closely associated with the Border

3rd Battalion Scots Guards, June 1944		Table 3

Battalion HQ

Cairngorm	(Commanding Officer)	*Brae Riach*	(Observation Post Tank)
Ben Lawers	(Second-in-Command)	*Ben Ledi*	(Observation Post Tank)
Ben Nevis	(Adjutant)	*Lochnagar*	(Observation Post Tank)
Ben Macdhui	(Officer-in-Charge, HQ Tanks)	*Kingdom of Fife*	(Armoured Command Vehicle)

Reconnaissance Troop (Stuarts)

Sandy Cameron	*Hielan' Laddie*	*Tullochgorm*
Criag-n'-Darroch	*The Black Bear*	*Ghillie Callum*
Killiecrankie	*Monymusk*	*Reel o' Tulloch*
Duntrune	*Corryhoylie*	*Sheepwife*

Scout Cars

Blue Bonnets	*Macbeth*	*Auld Reekie*
Colonsay	*Robert the Bruce*	*Rob Roy*
Glendaruel Highlander	*The Master of Ballantrae*	*Cock o' the North*
Killiecrankie	*The Black Douglas*	

Right Flank (Squadron)	**'S' Squadron**	**Left Flank (Squadron)**
Sqn. HQ	Sqn. HQ	Sqn. HQ
Greenock	*Coll*	*Esk*
Perth	*Tyree*	*Tweed*
Troon	*Mull*	*Teviot*
Crail	*Treshnish*	*Nith*
Oban (A.R.V.)	*Lewis* (A.R.V.)	*Tummel* (A.R.V.)
No. 1 Troop	No. 7 Troop	No. 11 Troop
Edinburgh	*Iona*	*Dee*
Dundee	*Rona*	*Don*
Ayr	*Canna*	*Deveron*
No. 2 Troop	No. 8 Troop	No. 12 Troop
Lochinvar	*Skye*	*Annan*
Inverness	*Uist*	*Beauly*
Dunkeld	*Barra*	*Findhorn*
No. 3 Troop	No. 9 Troop	No. 14 Troop
Stirling	*Jura*	*Spey*
Elgin	*Islay*	*Clyde*
Kirkcaldy	*Bute*	*Garry*
No. 4 Troop	No. 10 Troop	No. 15 Troop
Montrose	*Stroma*	*Lyon*
St. Andrews	*Staffa*	*Leven*
Glasgow	*Arran*	*Lochy*

▼89

89. *Cockermouth,* a Churchill of 110th Regiment, R.A.C. (Border), being entrained somewhere in Northern Command. The tank in front of it, *Athos,* belongs to another unit. (I.W.M.)

90. A Humber scout car named *Stork,* which belonged to a flame-throwing unit—141st Regiment, R.A.C. (The Buffs)—in Le Havre, September 1944. The vehicle's name, the unit code 993 complete with a white diagonal bar denoting G.HQ Troops, and the triangular sign of the 79th Armoured Division all appear on the glacis plate. (Note the twin Bren gun mounting for AA use, each fitted with a 100-round drum magazine.) (I.W.M.)

91. A Churchill II of 144th Regiment, R.A.C., being carefully loaded on to a tank transporter in the New Forest, 1942. Note the 3rd (Mixed) Division sign, the yellow 'A' Squadron triangle and the unit sign (white on brown) 68. The tank's name appears on the stowage bin on the turret side, but the only part visible is the first letter which is 'E'. Tanks at this time were finished in an all-over khaki-brown. (I.W.M.)

92. A Churchill III of 145th Regiment, R.A.C. (Duke of Wellington's), in Tunisia. This unit adopted a camouflage system of light-coloured stripes, perhaps a sand colour, over the basic dark green of its tanks, and took the more unusual precaution of bending back wireless aerials. (I.W.M.)

country of England. The C.O.'s tank was named *John Peel*, and *Ranter* was one of the Regimental HQ tanks. (*Ringwood* and *Bellman*, two more of John Peel's dogs, were to have been added but the tanks never materialized.) The carriers of the Reconnaissance Troop had the names of Cumbrian mountains (*Bowfell*, *Black Combe* and *Scafell*). Later, names associated with King Arthur, such as *Avalon*, were used. The tanks (Valentines and Churchills) in 'A', 'B' and 'C' Squadrons had local place-names beginning with the squadron letter; examples for 1st Troop, 'A' Squadron, are *Arnside*, *Appleby* and *Alston*.

111th Regiment, Royal Armoured Corps (Manchester): The Valentine tanks with which this Regiment (which did not leave the United Kingdom) was first equipped did not have names, but the Churchills issued later were named after British warships such as *Juno*, *Bulldog*, *Implacable*, *Renown* and *Furious*.

141st Regiment, Royal Armoured Corps (The Buffs): This unit was formed from the 7th Battalion, The Buffs, and took the letter 'S' (possibly for 'seven') for the names of its AFVs. (These were Churchills in 1942, only later were they equipped with the Crocodile flame-throwers with which they fought in north-west Europe.) Names for 7th Troop of 'B' Squadron were *Sabre*, *Sword* and *Scimitar*; and some scout cars were named *Spider*, *Stork* and *Seal*. At one time even Light Aid Detachment vehicles were christened; one example is *Samson*, a six-wheeled Austin breakdown lorry.

142nd Regiment, Royal Armoured Corps (Suffolk): Few details are available, but it is known that 'B' Squadron tanks were named after battles such as *Minden* and *Courtrai*.

▲94 ▼95

93. These Sherman tanks of 'B' Squadron, 144th Regiment, R.A.C., seen moving up to the front in Normandy, 1944, were never named, instead they were allocated serial numbers. Until August 1944 the 33rd Armoured Brigade was composed of 1st Northants Yeomanry, 144 and 148 R.A.C. Regiments; they were given the unit codes 173, 174 and 175 respectively. (I.W.M.)

94. *Nancy* and *Joan*, Churchill IIs of 4th Troop, 'C' Squadron and 5th Troop, 'B' Squadron (148th Regiment, R.A.C.), respectively, on a training exercise in the United Kingdom in 1942. (I.W.M.)

95. Lee tanks of 150th Regiment, R.A.C., in Burma in 1945. On the driver's hatch of the nearest tank is the name *Centurion*, and to the left of it is the tiger of the York and Lancaster Regiment. The Allied Star is on the hull side. These tanks would probably have been painted dark jungle green originally. (I.W.M.)

144th Regiment, Royal Armoured Corps (*East Lancashire*): This Regiment (renamed 4th Royal Tank Regiment on 1 March, 1945) reflected its origins as the East Lancashire Regiment by giving all its AFVs names beginning with 'El'; *Eloquent, Elusive, Ellerby, Elongator, Eligible* (these were all Churchills in 1942) and *Ely* (a Daimler scout car) are all examples. It must have been quite a task discovering or inventing over fifty names all with the prefix 'El', therefore when the Regiment was equipped with Sherman tanks for the D-Day campaign the habit of giving names was dropped. It was at this time that the Regiment adopted the practice of identifying individual tanks by displaying large serial numbers on both sides and rears of the turrets. These numbers were allocated in the following way (according to details kindly supplied by the former Adjutant of the Regiment, Captain E. C. Robinson). The Stuarts of Reconnaissance Troop were given the numbers from 1 to 11; AA Troop's Crusaders, Nos. 12-17; Regimental HQs Shermans, Nos. 20-23; 'A' Squadron's Shermans, Nos. 30-49; 'B' Squadron's Shermans, Nos. 50-69; 'C' Squadron's Shermans, Nos. 70-89; and Nos. 18-19 and 24-29 were allocated for spare tanks.

145th Regiment, Royal Armoured Corps (*Duke of Wellington's*): The letter 'D', probably chosen because of its association with the initial letter of its former title, was used for the AFVs of this Regiment. Some, or all, of the Regimental HQ tanks are believed to have had names beginning 'Duke of . . .'. Various names were used by the squadrons, such as *Dorothy* (a Churchill of 14th Troop 'C' Squadron in Tunisia); and *Deserter*, a German Panther tank captured in Italy. The Churchills of this Regiment were doubly distinctive—not only did they have a very unusual camouflage scheme (adopted during the Tunisian campaign) but their wireless aerials were also bent backwards thereby reducing the height and making them less conspicuous in, say, a hull-down position.

147th Regiment, Royal Armoured Corps (*Hampshire*): This Regiment, when converted from infantry, was equipped with Churchill tanks. The Regimental HQ tanks bore the names of Hampshire Regiment battle honours; examples are *Minden* (the C.O.'s tank), *Oudenarde, India* and *Hellas*. 'A' Squadron's tank names began with the letter 'R'; the troops taking the vowels in order, thus: 1st Troop —Ra . . .; 2nd Troop—Re . . .; 3rd Troop —Ri . . . (*Rightful, Ringwood* and *Rival*); 4th Troop—Ro . . .; and 5th Troop—Ru . . . The names of 'B' Squadron tanks all began with an 'S'; the troops again taking the vowels in order—Sa, Se, Si, etc. 'C. Squadron tanks' names began with a 'T'

and followed the same vowel sequence as in 'A' and 'B' Squadrons.

148th Regiment, Royal Armoured Corps: Girls' names were used for the Churchill tanks of this Regiment. In this system the five troops of 'A' Squadron were allotted names beginning, respectively, 'A' to 'E' (*Agatha, Bertha, Celia* etc.). 'B' Squadron troops were given the letters 'F' to 'J', and 'C' Squadron had 'K' to 'O'. *Penelope* and *Patricia* are examples of names given to Regimental HQ's tanks.

150th Regiment, Royal Armoured Corps (*York and Lancaster*): Details of naming systems used by this Regiment are only available for 'C' Squadron, which was equipped with Lee and Grant tanks and saw action in Burma between 1944 and 1945. The tanks of 'C' Squadron used names beginning with the letter 'C' (*Cavalier, Caledonian, Centurion* and *Cannon*) and on some tanks a tiger (passant) was shown on the left side of the front plate of the hull. This symbol was taken from the cap badge worn by the York and Lancaster Regiment and its use was a minor infringement of the War Office order of 1942, which stated that regimental crests or titles should not be displayed on vehicles.

153rd Regiment, Royal Armoured Corps (*Essex*): The Churchill tanks used by this Regiment, which fought in Normandy until August 1944 when it was disbanded, were mainly given Essex place-names. 'A' Squadron's tanks all used names beginning with the letter 'N', and the vowels that followed were allocated to the five troops of the Squadron; examples are *Navestock, Nayland* and *Nazeing* (tanks of 1st Troop); and *Nuneaton* and *Nunehead* (tanks belonging to 5th Troop). Names used by 'B' Squadron began with the letter 'B' (*Bapaume, Billericay* and *Bishops Stortford*); and 'C' Squadron (in 1944 this Squadron was transferred to 107th Regiment, R.A.C., although the men were allowed to retain their Essex Regiment cap badges) is believed to have been allotted the letter 'C'. Regimental HQ tanks were named after Essex Regiment battle honours such as *Alma, Taku* and *Waterloo*.

157th Regiment, Royal Armoured Corps (*Hampshire*); This unit only existed as an armoured regiment from November 1941 to August 1943. Little is known of their naming system except that the C.O.'s tank was named *Haking* (after the then Colonel of the Hampshire Regiment, General Sir Richard Haking), and that other names used were *Horatius, Heedless, Hannibal* and *Hallidon*.

8. The Reconnaissance Corps
The Reconnaissance Corps was renamed the Reconnaissance Regiment when it was

incorporated into the Royal Armoured Corps in January 1944 and retained this title until it was disbanded in August 1946. The battalions of the Reconnaissance Corps were equipped with many armoured vehicles, including carriers, light reconnaissance cars and armoured cars, and these were often given individual names. Details of some of the battalions are given below.

3rd Battalion Reconnaissance Corps: Examples of some of the names used for the AFVs of this Battalion in September 1942 are as follows: *Archangel* (Squadron Leader), *Adventure, Adamant, Avenger, Arrow, Alnwick, Ark Royal, America, Anxiety, Arcadian, Antelope, Assassin* and *Annapola* (all Humber light reconnaissance cars of 'A' Squadron); *Actor, Amiens, Arras, Action, Astra, Achilles, Arcas, Arizona, Abbeville, Aeason, Aix, Aggressor, Auk, Appollo* (sic) and *Ajax* (all Universal Carriers of 'A' Squadron). 'A' Squadron's sign was a red/blue/white rectangle divided horizontally, and was, like those of the other squadrons, unique to this Battalion. Examples of names used by 'B' Squadron are *Boadicea* (Squadron Leader), *Buzzard, Battledore, Bastianado, Bludgeon, Bolas, Broadsword, Boomerang, Bluebird, Bullfinch* and *Batwing* (all Humber light reconnaissance cars); *Buzzard, Bosco, Beau Geste, Bahram, Basilius, Buffalo, Belon, Bruno, Belcius, Bison, Bellona, Bronco* and *Belsarius* (all Universal Carriers). 'B' Squadron's sign was a red/white/red rectangle divided horizontally. The following names are examples of those given by 'C' Squadron to their Humber light reconnaissance cars; these are *Cromwell, Campaigner* and *Curious* (all belonging to IX Troop); and *Comet* (belonging to X Troop). Examples of names given to Universal Carriers of the same Squadron are *Cobra* and *Corncrake* (belonging to IX Troop); *Cassius* (belonging to XI Troop); *Circe* and *Cyclops*. The Squadron sign was a yellow/blue/yellow rectangle horizontally divided, with the troop number in roman numerals on the centre strip.

4th Battalion Reconnaissance Corps: During the early part of 1942, two of the Humber light reconnaissance cars of 'B' Squadron were named *Skua* and *Puffin*. Other names given to the AFVs of this Battalion were those of battles and warships—*Blenheim, Crecy, Meggiddo, Formidable* and *Revenge* (the latter was a Humber armoured car used in Italy). In early 1942 the Battalion had the unit code sign 991, which was in white on a rectangle divided horizontally green/blue; later they adopted the familiar number 41 used for most Reconnaissance Corps Battalions. The unit also used a black panther badge on a diagonally divided yellow/light green

▲96

▲97 ▼98

rectangle on its vehicles, and this was retained as a unit badge through the Regiment's Italian campaign.

49th Battalion Reconnaissance Corps: Various names were used for the AFVs of this unit. During 3rd Troop's ('A' Squadron) time in Holland, towards the end of the Second World War, names used by them were *Skiddaw, Snowdon* (Humber Mark IV armoured cars), *Paris* and *Pegasus* (Humber light reconnaissance cars). An example of a name used by 'D' Squadron is *Sir Launcelot* (a light reconnaissance car).

56th Battalion Reconnaissance Corps: This Battalion, which formed part of the 78th Division in Tunisia in 1942, had a strong Irish connection and this is reflected in some of the names given to their AFVs: *Faugh-a-Ballagh* (this means 'Clear the Way' and was the motto of the Royal Irish Fusiliers) was the name given to the Commanding Officer's Humber Mark III light reconnaissance car. The light reconnaissance cars belonging to the leaders of 'A', 'B' and 'C' Squadrons, were named respectively *Atholl, Buaidh-go-Beage II* and *Clarew*. Other names used by carriers and light reconnaissance cars of the Battalion followed the squadron letter; examples are *Alert, Aristotle, Acorn, Blenheim* and *Bacchus*.

G.HQ Liaison Regiment: Usually known as the 'Phantom Regiment', this unit's armoured fighting vehicles employed various naming systems at different times. 'A' Squadron used the names of famous express trains; 'F' Squadron's AFVs were at one time given the names of ballets; and some squadrons used Derby or Grand National racehorses names. Eventually, all squadrons adopted the same system of using the names of British birds; an example is *Raven* which was a Humber Mark III light reconnaissance car belonging to 'A' Squadron. The following are names known to have been used by various squadrons of this Regiment: *L's Angel* (a Humber light reconnaissance car of 'L' Squadron); *Spooks 1st* (a White scout car used by 'A' Squadron in north-west Europe during 1945); and *North Wind, South Wind, East Wind, Beaufort* and *Belvoir* (all Daimler scout cars).

96. Universal Carriers of 3rd Battalion, Reconnaissance Corps, exercising in the United Kingdom in 1941. The nearest vehicle is *Bronco* and behind it is *Bulldog*. (I.W.M.)

97. Men of the 49th Reconnaissance Regiment receiving a jubilant welcome from the citizens of Utrecht in 1945. The Humber Mark IV armoured car (W.D. No. F 133751) belongs to 'A' Squadron. Its name, *Skiddaw*, can be seen behind the white tactical sign on the turret. (Planet News)

98. *Flying Scotsman*, a Mark IA W/T scout car belonging to 'A' Squadron, G.HQ Liaison Regiment, in 1942. (The Times)

▲100 ▼101

99. A Sherman command tank of Headquarters, 5th Guards Armoured Brigade, in Holland, 1944. Behind *Snow White* (whose portrait as well as name appears on the nose plate) are vehicles of 3rd Battalion Irish Guards (32nd Guards Brigade) and a Daimler armoured car of 2nd Household Cavalry Regiment. (P.N.A.)

100. *Jenny the Creme Cracker*, the AEC armoured command vehicle belonging to the Commander, Royal Electrical and Mechanical Engineers of 7th Armoured Division, in north-west Europe in about 1944. The vehicle's name is on the nose plate and the W.D. number (F 89236) is shown on the side of the bonnet. (A.E.C.)

101. A Crusader AA tank of Headquarters, 22nd Armoured Brigade, coming ashore in Normandy, 1944. The name *Allahkeef* and the Allied Star can be seen on the turret. Overall dimensions of the vehicle, the unit mobilization number and the number of the landing craft all appear on the front track-guard for shipping purposes. (I.W.M.)

9. Armoured Formation Headquarters

The tanks, scout cars and armoured command vehicles of armoured division and brigade headquarters were often named; these names tended to be more permanent than those used by the armoured regiments where AFV and personnel losses were much heavier.

5th Guards Armoured Brigade: Little is known of the names used by this Brigade, and the only example available is of a Sherman named *Snow White*. Incidentally, the HQ tanks of this formation in 1944 were distinguished unusually by large letters (such as 'F', 'G' and 'H') on their turrets.

6th Guards Tank Brigade: The Churchill tanks of this Brigade were named *St. David, Vengeance, Vindictive, Victory* and *Valiant*; the armoured command vehicles were given the names *St. George* and *St. Andrew*; and the three Churchill bridgelayers were named *Forth Bridge, London Bridge* and *Brooklyn Bridge*. All the Brigade's scout cars were named after hunts beginning with the letter 'B', such as *Blankney, Beaufort* and *Brecon*.

6th Armoured Division: In 1941 the HQ Squadron of this Division used the names of *Snow White* and the Seven Dwarfs (*Sneezy, Doc, Dopey, Happy, Sleepy, Bashful* and *Grumpy*) for its Valentines; these names were still being used by them in Palestine in 1945, even though, by this time, the Squadron was equipped with Staghound armoured cars and had been renamed HQ 1st Armoured Division.

7th Armoured Brigade: The Crusader tanks used in the Western Desert by HQ of this Brigade were all named after warships of the 14th Destroyer Flotilla, for example *Jervis, Javelin, Jaguar, Janus* and *Jersey*. This particular naming system was chosen because the Flotilla's Commander was a friend of the Brigade Commander, Brigadier G. M. O. Davey.

7th Armoured Division: *Vengeance* was the name given to the G.O.C.'s Sherman tank used in the north-west Europe campaign. Rather less frightening names were allocated to the A.E.C. armoured command vehicles such as *Mabel Crumb* (A C V 1) and *Jenny the Creme Cracker* (the R.E.M.E. Commander's A C V).

9th Armoured Division: In 1942 this Division's G.O.C. was the exuberant General Horrocks whose Covenanter tank was named *Panda*. The Divisional sign was a panda's head—said to have been used as a pun on the name of the German Panzer divisions.

11th Armoured Division: The formation sign of this Division was a bull, which probably explains why the G.O.C.'s Crusader tank was named *Taurus* (this was later replaced by *Taurus II*, a Cromwell).

▲102

Other Cromwells used were *Taureg II* and *Oliver*—the latter probably being a pun on the type name of the tank.

10. Miscellaneous British Units using Armoured Fighting Vehicles

THE ROYAL ENGINEERS

The Royal Engineers Assault Squadrons were formed to operate the Churchill AVRE which had been developed in 1943 to be used on demolition and bridge-laying operations. 77th Assault Squadron was equipped with Buffaloes (tracked landing vehicles), used in the latter stages of the war in north-west Europe, and these vehicles bore names, together with symbols, denoting their position in the squadron (*Argosy* 2C, *Cutter* 2H, *Esquay* 1A and *Rouvres* 2A). Other names given to AVREs were *Sabre* and *Scimitar*—both in the same troop of 222nd Assault Squadron.

THE ROYAL MARINES

The Reconnaissance Battalion of the Royal Marine Division was equipped with Mark VIC light tanks and Daimler scout cars as well as Universal Carriers in 1941. One of the unit's light tanks at this time was named *Springbok*. Later, the Royal Marine Division was broken up, but one of its progeny was the Royal Marine Armoured Support Group which was formed early in 1944 to provide close inshore fire-support for the D-Day landings. This formation was equipped with a total of eighty Centaur tanks, fitted with 95mm howitzers, and twenty Sherman control tanks. The tanks were carried in landing craft from which, hove-to off the beaches, they gave supporting fire to the assault troops; and were later used to give support inland. This Support Group was organized in two regiments, each of two batteries with four troops (each troop consisted of four Centaurs and one Sherman control tank) and one independent battery (the 5th). The names used by these tanks mostly followed the troop letter; examples are *Hunter* (a Centaur of 2nd Battery), *Seawolf* (a Centaur of 5th Battery), and *Fox* (a Sherman of 'F' Troop, 2nd Battery).

THE ROYAL ARTILLERY

Self-propelled guns and command tanks of the Royal Artillery were often named in a similar fashion to those in armoured regiments—this point is well illustrated by examples of naming systems used in the following two regiments.

147th Field Regiment (*Essex Yeomanry*): This Regiment comprised three batteries: No. 431 ('A' and 'B' Troops); No. 413 ('C' and 'D' Troops); and No. 511 ('E' and 'F' Troops). During the north-east Europe campaign, each battery was equipped with Sherman Command and O.P. tanks. These vehicles usually bore the names of places in Essex or, later, of places where the Regiment had seen action; some examples of names adopted which followed the Troop letters are *Bramley* (a Sherman O.P. used by the Commander of 'B' Troop); *Brentwood* (a Sexton); *Dobbs Weir* (a Sherman O.P. tank); and *Debden*, *Falaise* and *Fontenay* (all Sextons).

91st Anti-Tank Regiment: Converted from a Scottish infantry battalion (the 5th Battalion Argyll and Sutherland Highlanders) this Regiment used, not unsurprisingly, Scottish place-names for its vehicles. The self-propelled batteries were numbered 144 and 146 and equipped with Achilles M-10s. The command tank of 144th Battery was not named, but the M-10s were named as follows: *Aberdeen*, *Angus*, *Argyll* and *Ayr* ('A' Troop); *Barra*, *Benbecula*, *Borreray* and *Bute* ('B' Troop); and *Cairngorm*, *Coulbeg*, *Cramalt* and *Cruachan* ('C' Troop). *Zadig* was the name used by 146th Battery for their command tank, and the names adopted by individual troops were as follows: *Glencoe. Glengarry, Glenaffric* and *Glendaruel* ('G' Troop); *Hawick, Hamilton* and *Huntly* ('H' Troop); and *Invergordon, Inverness, Invergarry* and *Inverarary* ('I' Troop). (These were later

102. An AVRE with an SBG bridge accompanying Churchill tanks in the assault on Le Havre, September 1944. The AVRE is named *Sepoy* (Regimental No. 1C) and belongs to 222 Assault Squadron of 42nd Assault Regiment, Royal Enginners. The unit code, 1235 in white on a light blue rectangle, and the 79th Armoured Division sign are both on the AVRE's rear plate. (I.W.M.)

103. *Seawolf* and other Centaur IVs (equipped with 95mm howitzers) of 'S' Troop, 5th Independent Royal Marine Armoured Support Battery, making final preparations for D-Day. Note the degrees marked around the turret top for fire-control purposes. (I.W.M.)

104. The Essex Yeomanry in action in Germany with *Brentwood*, a Sexton SP 25 gun of 431 Battery, 147th Field Regiment, Royal Artillery. This Regiment was attached to 8th Armoured Brigade. (I.W.M.)

105. A Lanchester armoured car, *Blair Castle*, being used as a' machine-gun carrier by men of 2nd Battalion Argyll and Sutherland Highlanders on an exercise in Malaya in 1941. The W.D. number is 465 but is shown in the local style. (I.W.M.)

▲103

changed to *Loch Libo, Loch Ness, Loch Lomond* and *Loch Maddy* respectively.) The gun tractors in the two towed batteries (Nos. 145 and 344) also carried names.

INFANTRY

Nearly all British infantry battalions in the Second World War employed tracked armoured carriers of the Universal type for various duties. These vehicles were frequently named, but the subject is a vast one and is really outside the scope of this survey. A rare example of an infantry battalion using armoured cars is the 2nd Battalion Argyll and Sutherland Highlanders. While in Malaya in 1941-42 this Regiment had a platoon of four Lanchester and three Marmon-Herrington armoured cars. Names given to some of these (mostly Lanchesters) were of castles, such as *Glamis Castle, Stirling Castle, Edinburgh Castle, Blair Castle* and (an English interloper among Scottish strongholds) *Arundel Castle.*

11. British Commonwealth Armoured Units

Prior to the Second World War even major Commonwealth countries, like Canada and Australia, had only small token armoured forces, although these were expanded greatly during the War. In many cases Commonwealth armoured units

▲104 ▼105

106. Sherman tanks belonging to 5th Canadian Armoured Regiment (8th Princess Louise's New Brunswick Hussars), practice firing on enemy positions near Ravenna in December 1944. The second vehicle in this line is *Bullseye* of 2nd Troop, 'B' Squadron. (I.W.M.)

107. Tanks of 12th Canadian Armoured Regiment (Three Rivers Regiment) preparing to fire on a snipers nest during the battle for the Italian town of Ortona in December 1943. The nearest Sherman is *Challenger* of 'C' Squadron—note the red/white/red recognition mark still shown on the hull side and the duplication of the W.D. number T 147291. This is explained by the interchanging of AFVs, which was a regular practice between British and Canadian units. (I.W.M.)

followed the British practice of giving names to individual vehicles—some examples are given below.

CANADA

2nd Armoured Regiment, Lord Strathcona's Horse: This Regiment, which formed part of the 5th Canadian Armoured Division, was equipped with Shermans in both Italy and north-west Europe. A list of names used for these vehicles is given in Table 4, and it should be noted that where four names are shown for a troop, one of these is a replacement tank which has been renamed. In many other cases replacements were not renamed, but inherited the name of the preceding tank. The same name was sometimes used for as many as four replacements; *Claresholm IV* was an example.

11th Armoured Regiment (The Ontario Regiment), 12th Armoured Regiment (Three Rivers Regiment), 14th Armoured Regiment (Calgary Regiment): These three units formed the 1st Canadian Army Tank Brigade and were equipped with Churchill tanks (some of Calgary Regiment's Churchills took part in the raid on Dieppe). It was only later when renamed the 1st Canadian Armoured Brigade that the formation used Shermans.

All three Regiments used names following the squadron letter for their 'A', 'B' and 'C' Squadrons; examples are *Cartier, Columbus* and *Cabot* (6th Troop, 'C' Squadron, 11th Armoured Regiment); *Achilles, Anthony* and *Arthur* ('A' Squadron, 12th Armoured Regiment); and *Beefy, Bellicose* and *Bert* (some 'B' Squadron Churchills of the 14th Armoured Regiment lost at Dieppe). The Regimental HQ tanks of the 11th Armoured Regiment were named after racehorses such as *Sea Biscuit, Exterminator* (one of these two was renamed *Sun Chariot* early in 1942 after George VI's visit to the Regiment), *War Admiral* and *Man-o'-War*. The 14th Armoured Regiment's R.HQ tanks seem to have borne names which began with the letter 'R'; one example is *Ringer*.

AUSTRALIA

The pre-War 1st and 2nd Australian Tank Companies, equipped with Mark VIB light tanks, used names of Australian birds and animals, respectively; examples are *Bower Bird, Kookaburra, Wombat* and *Wallaby*. Weapons and birds were the name subjects adopted by the 1st and 2nd Australian Armoured Car Companies of the militia. Both Companies were equipped with Australian-made Ford armoured cars. During the Second World War the Royal Australian Armoured Corps at one time amounted to three armoured divisions. Later it was reduced to a number of

2nd Armoured Regiment, Lord Strathcona's Horse			Table 4
Regimental HQ			
Strathcona (Commanding Officer)		*Scimitar* (R.HQ Troop Leader)	
Screwball (Second-in-Command)		*Spartan* (Tp.Sgt)	

'A' Squadron	**'B' Squadron**	**'C' Squadron**
HQ Fighting	HQ Fighting	HQ Fighting
Akbar	*Brown*	*Churchill*
Abdul	*Bader*	*Confucius*
Attila	*Bishop*	*Connolly*
Ajax	*Barker*	*Conacher*
1st Troop	1st Troop	1st Troop
Alligator	*Beaver*	*Cougar*
Antelope	*Buffalo*	*Condor*
Armadillo	*Broncho*	*Cobra*
	Bear	*Caribou*
2nd Troop	2nd Troop	2nd Troop
Aspen	*Balsam*	*Capri*
Alder	*Bluebell/Briar*	*Cork*
Almond	*Buttercup*	*Crete*
Apricot	*Birch*	*China*
3rd Troop	3rd Troop	3rd Troop
Algiers	*Biscay*	*Chicontimi*
Athens	*Bengal*	*Chippewa*
Alaska	*Baltic*	*Chilliwack*
	Bering	*Chinook*
4th Troop	4th Troop	4th Troop
Algonquin	*Banff*	*Camrose*
Alberta	*Barrie*	*Calgary*
Aldershot	*Brandon*	*Claresholm*
Argyle	*Broadview*	*Canmore*

▲108 ▼109

108. A much-photographed tank, *Bert*, a Churchill III of 'B' Squadron, 14th Canadian Tank Regiment (Calgary Regiment), disabled and captured in the Dieppe Raid, August 1942. The ram and maple leaf sign of 1st Canadian Tank Brigade appears on the nose plate.

109. A Matilda Frog flame-thrower of 6th Troop, 2/1st Armoured Brigade Reconnaissance Squadron at Balikpapan, Borneo, July 1945. The inverted triangle denoting an independent squadron is on the turret and the unit's number 2-1 appears just behind the driver's vision port, with the 4th Australian Armoured Brigade's crocodile and palm sign to the right. The camouflage colour used is jungle green. (Australian Official)

110. *Bidar*, a Sherman of R.HQ, 9th Royal Deccan Horse, in Burma, 1945. This Regiment was the third armoured regiment in 255th Indian Tank Brigade, the other two were 116th Regiment, R.A.C., and 5th Probyn's Horse, and the code sign was 53. (I.W.M.)

111. A rare photograph of *Tipperary Tim*, a Humber Mark I armoured car belonging to 19th King George V's Own Lancers, in India in 1942. (Regimental History)

112. A locally-built Chevrolet Fortress armoured car of the Kenya Armoured Car Regiment in the East African campaign of 1940-41. The Regiment's leopard badge appears below the sign C13, which denoted that this car was the 13th in 'C' Squadron. Girls names beginning with the squadron letter were often used for AFVs and were in many cases displayed on a small raised metal plaque, as here, on the hull side above the vision slit beside the driver. (I.W.M.)

▲110 ▼111

▼112

armoured brigades, some units of which fought in New Guinea and Borneo. In 1945 these brigades were equipped with Matildas and names generally followed the squadron letters; some examples from 'C' Squadron, 2/4th Australian Armoured Regiment are *Cobar*, *Cairns* and *Casino* (13th Troop); *Carlton*, *Castlemaine* and *Cascade* (14th Troop); and *Cavalier*, *Calliope* and *Courageous* (15th Troop).

INDIA

Mechanization of the (British) Indian Army started in about 1938 with the conversion of some cavalry regiments to armoured cars or light tanks. During the War, three Indian Armoured Divisions were formed, although not all were in existence simultaneously, and reinforcement problems led to some confusing amalgamations and transfers of armoured brigades. Armoured Car Regiments and Reconnaissance units for Infantry Divisions also formed part of the Indian Armoured Corps. Armoured fighting vehicles were named in many regiments and various systems were used: a few examples of these systems are given below.

5th Probyn's Horse: The names of this Regiment's old chargers were perpetuated in the tanks with which the Regiment was equipped. Horses names used were *Alred*, *Anzac* ('A' Squadron), *Bob* and *Bayard* ('B' Squadron).

9th Royal Deccan Horse: This Regiment used Indian place-names for its tanks such as *Bidar* (R.HQ), *Patiala* and *Ferozepore* ('A' Squadron).

The Scinde Horse (14th Prince of Wales's Own Cavalry): The Scinde Horse served in Persia and Syria between 1942 and 1945. First equipped with wheeled carriers they were later given Stuart and Sherman tanks. Regimental HQ armoured fighting vehicles bore the name *Jacob* (after John Jacob, a distinguished early commanding officer of the Regiment) and names of Regimental battle honours; an example is *Meeanee*. Armoured fighting vehicles of the three 'sabre' squadrons were named after places and rivers in India (some of which are now in Pakistan) such as *Kurram*, *Beas*, *Chenab* and *Shahalam*.

19th King George V's Own Lancers: The armoured cars of this Regiment's 'A' Squadron in India in 1942 were named after Grand National winners—*Tipperary Tim*, *Golden Miller* and *Austerlitz*. The latter was the cause of some disappointment to a visiting French officer when he learned that Napoleon's victory was not in mind when the name was chosen.

KENYA

Kenya Armoured Car Regiment: This locally-raised unit, which played a useful part in the East African campaign in 1941, was at first equipped with armoured cars designed and built in Kenya although later South African-made Marmon-Herringtons were used. Full details are not available, but names, mostly of girls, beginning with the squadron letter were used. The Kenya-built cars displayed these names on raised metal plaques; some examples are *Boadicea*, *Bella*, *Billie* and *Buster* ('B' Squadron); *Christobel*, *Clara* and *Celia* ('C' Squadron).

AFV MARKINGS
BRITISH AND COMMONWEALTH

1914-18

The squadron, section and individual vehicle symbols adopted for the armoured cars of the Royal Naval Air Service Armoured Car Division in 1914 have already been referred to. This system (for example 8A2 stands for No. 8 Squadron 'A' Section, 2nd car, a Rolls-Royce armoured car) was not adopted by the Army—perhaps because it was felt that it gave away too much information to the enemy. The naval armoured cars also carried the large letters R.N.A.S., either in white, dark grey/black or (possibly) red, according to the shade of the vehicle itself. Army armoured cars and the R.N.A.S. cars taken over by the Army in late 1915, usually showed their War Department numbers at the front or sides of the bonnet and at the rear of the vehicle. These numbers were prefixed by one or two letters, usually 'LC', 'C' or 'M', and the War Department arrow; for example LC ↑1528, was a Rolls-Royce armoured car belonging to a section formerly of No. 1 Squadron, R.N.A.S. operating with the Army in German East Africa. Before this practice became fairly universal, armoured cars supplied to both the R.N.A.S. and the Army often bore civil registration marks to the county of their registration.

The R.N.A.S. armoured car squadrons sent to Russia in 1916 were not taken over by the Army and continued, for a time at least, to use squadron/section/vehicle markings, supplemented by coloured roundels, as distinguishing marks. In 1918, an instruction was issued that War

Office vehicles were to bear civilian-type registrations, these consisted of a number followed by the letters 'B' or 'C', with combinations 'CA', 'CB' etc.

British tanks nearly always showed their individual War Department numbers, usually in white, on the hull sides near the rear. These were without a prefix except in the case of Mark A Mediums, which had a separate series prefixed 'A', and gun carriers which had the prefix 'GC'. The numbers started at 500 for Mark I tanks and, by the end of the war, were running in the 10,000s for heavy tanks. Both medium tanks and gun carriers had numbers below 500. Supply tanks—both converted Marks I-IV tanks and modified gun carriers—had the word 'supply' painted on the hull sides.

The system in many battalions of the Tank Corps, that of showing the battalion letter followed by the number of the tank in the battalion, has been referred to earlier (see page 8). This was the only fairly consistent tactical marking in use during the First World War. Some signs used by individual units have already been noted. A tactical sign used for a particular occasion—the Cambrai battle of 1917—was the large letters 'WC' on the rear of tanks designated for wire cutting in the assault.

In 1918 an identification mark consisting of vertical white/red/white strips was painted on all British tanks and armoured cars except those in the Middle East and Russia. This mark was usually on the sides of the front 'horns' on tanks and in the

form of a rectangle on the hull sides on armoured cars; in some cases the coloured strips were also added to front rear and top surfaces.

1919-38

After the war, wartime armoured fighting vehicles still in service retained their W.D. Numbers and, where appropriate, the 1918-style civilian registration. New or rebuilt Rolls-Royce armoured cars used by the Tank Corps at first had W.D. numbers prefixed by the letters 'TC', and then the prefix 'M' (in common with staff cars) was allotted. The Peerless armoured cars built in 1919 had an 'L' prefix. In 1920-21 various experimental medium and light tanks were given numbers between 1 and 66, although these do not appear to have been shown externally on the vehicles. Between 1921 and 1923 concurrent series' for Vickers light (later re-classified medium) tanks and Dragon artillery tractors were allotted. These numbers ran from Nos. 1 to 48 for Dragons and from Nos. 1 to 60 for tanks, before it was decided in 1924 to maintain one sequence for all 'A' vehicles. 'A' vehicles comprised all armoured fighting vehicles, including armoured cars, as well as tracked towing vehicles such as Dragons and semi-tracked vehicles which, in most cases, were unarmoured. Letter prefixes were then allocated to the different types, for example 'T' for tanks, 'D' for Dragons and 'H' for semi-tracks. Armoured cars retained the 'M' prefix although this was changed to 'F' in about 1931. 'T' and 'D'

▼113

▼114

▲115 ▼116

113. A picture taken after the First World War, but clearly showing the white/red/white recognition sign painted on the horns of this tank, which is a Mark IV with 'tadpole' tail. The W.D. number 9001 is also very distinct. (I.W.M.)

114. The gun carrier *Kingston* which was adapted to carry supplies of a Gun Carrier Company in France, 1918. The recognition sign can be seen on the front horns, and the word 'Supply' together with the W.D. number, prefixed 'GC', are near the rear of the hull. (I.W.M.)

115. Six-wheeled Lanchester Mark IIA (the nearest vehicle) and Mark I armoured cars belonging to the 12th Royal Lancers in about 1938. Note the Regimental badge and pennant shown on the turrets, the unit's abbreviation ('12.L'), the W.D. number, and letter 'A' in red (denoting 'A' vehicle), partly obscured by the pickaxe, on the hull side, and the civil registration mark on the front of the bonnet. The overall colour was probably deep bronze-green. (I.W.M.)

116. *Davenport*, a Humber armoured car of 'D' Squadron, 161st (Green Howards) Reconnaissance Regiment, in Northern Ireland. The Squadron's bar symbol plus the troop number 3 are on the glacis plate beside the driver's port. Despite the camouflage net the car's name, W.D. number, bridge group sign, unit code and Northern Ireland Troops sign all appear clearly.

prefixes were given, retrospectively, to tanks and Dragons already allocated numbers.

War Department numbers were usually shown in small white figures on the hull sides, but sometimes they were displayed, either additionally or simply as an alternative, on the front or at the rear of tanks. The exception to this rule was 2nd Battalion Royal Tank Corps already referred to (see page 8). Civilian registrations (index marks) were also allocated to, and shown on, W.D. vehicles during the inter-war period. These were all allocated by the County of Middlesex Licensing Authority; examples are H.1088, W.D. No. T.19 (Mark I medium tank); and BMM 134, W.D. No. T. 1357 (Mark IV light tank). Plates of the usual type and size used for civilian vehicles bore these registrations, which were carried at the front and rear of the AFVs.

During this period, from 1927 onwards, tanks, armoured cars and Dragons were supposed to be distinguished by a large letter 'A' in red to denote that they were 'A', or fighting, vehicles. Despite this it was not always shown on tanks. Unit code signs were not used at this time, but the unit's name was shown in an abbreviated form. This was often stencilled in white above the W.D. number; for example 3RTC
T   a Mark II Medium of the 3rd
138

Battalion, Royal Tank Corps. Official abbreviations were laid down for each unit although they do not always appear to have been adhered to. Cavalry regiments, when mechanized, usually painted their regimental badge on the turrets of their tanks. Armoured cars and light tanks of the Royal Tank Corps in India were allotted Government of India registration numbers prefixed by a broad arrow.

About 1931 a new system of tactical signs was introduced for the Royal Tank Corps. This consisted of a circular symbol for 'A' Company; the form of a solid disc for No. 1 Section; a ring for No. 2 Section; and a ring with a small disc in the centre for No. 3 Section. A triangle, with similar variants for the Sections was used for 'B' Company; and a diamond with variants for 'C' Company. The Company HQ tanks had the letter 'A', 'B' or 'C', as appropriate, superimposed on the symbol. Battalion headquarters tanks had an oblong symbol in the R.T.C. colours with the battalion number in the centre. Within a few years further geometric symbols such as inverted triangles, semi-circles and squares made their appearance and were used by some tank battalions.

1939-45
A few months before the outbreak of the Second World War a new system of tactical markings for tanks was laid down by the War Office. A diamond shape was

to be used for Battalion Headquarters; a triangle for 'A' Company or Squadron; a square for 'B' Company or Squadron; and a circle for 'C' Company or Squadron. The colours to be used were as follows: Battalion HQ was to use battalion colours; 'A' Company, red; 'B' Company, yellow; and 'C' Company, blue. Company letters or section numbers were to be painted in black in the centre of the sign. The signs were to be made from tin plate and carried at the rear of the tanks, and sizes varied from approximately 9 inches in height, for light tanks and Infantry Mark Is, to 18 inches for others. This idea does not appear to have been widely adopted, if at all, and the whole system was soon modified into the simpler form of painting the symbols directly on to the vehicles.

By mid-1940 the following system was more-or-less in general use, although the details were at the discretion of formation and/or regimental commanders. Battalion or regimental headquarters used a hollow diamond; 'A' Company or Squadron a hollow triangle; 'B' Company or Squadron a hollow square; and 'C' Company or Squadron a hollow circle or ring. Later, when armoured car regiments had a fourth squadron, a vertical bar was allocated as the distinguishing sign.

The colour of these tactical signs was then uniform throughout the whole unit with colour differences denoting the position of the unit in the formation. Red

117▼

tactical signs denoted the senior battalion/ regiment in the brigade; yellow tactical signs denoted the second battalion/ regiment in the brigade; blue tactical signs denoted the third battalion/regiment in the brigade; and green tactical signs denoted the fourth battalion/regiment in the brigade. (In a British armoured brigade, the fourth unit was normally the infantry motor battalion.) Unbrigaded units were supposed to carry white tactical signs, but this colour seems to have been unpopular in battle and was often avoided as being rather too conspicuous. The tactical signs and colours just mentioned appear to have been adhered to although there were exceptions. One example is the 5th Royal Tank Regiment, which during 1940-41 is recorded as having purple tactical signs.

War Department numbers continued to be carried on British military vehicles throughout the Second World War, but shortly after the War's commencement, civilian index marks were no longer allotted and existing plates were not replaced. The prefixes 'T' for tank and 'F' for armoured car were continued although the latter was extended to include scout cars and other categories of wheeled armoured vehicles. Dragons as a class were soon superseded, and in some cases their function was taken over by carriers of the Loyd or Universal type which had the prefix 'T'. New classes introduced during

the War were 'S' for self-propelled guns (both tracked and wheeled); 'P' for amphibious cargo carriers (including Buffaloes); and 'REC' for armoured recovery vehicles. Light reconnaissance cars were prefixed 'M'; and armoured vehicles, mounted on what were basically truck or lorry chassis (such as wheeled armoured personnel carriers and armoured command vehicles), carried the prefixes 'Z' or 'L' respectively—later, ACVs adopted the 'F' prefix.

Canadian-built vehicles, constructed to Canadian Army orders, carried the prefix 'C' before the W.D. No.; for example CF61807 (a Lynx scout car). Suffix letters were added to the W.D. numbers of many Churchill tanks during the War to denote various re-works, and the suffix 'DD' denoted a DD (amphibious) Valentine or Sherman.

At the outbreak of the Second World War, unit titles shown on vehicles (as described above) were painted-out in accordance with standing instructions. Unit code signs were introduced in their place and, in general, this system identified the unit according to its position in the formation to which it belonged. Therefore, in most cases the code signs were unique only in conjunction with the formation signs, which also had to be displayed on the vehicle. The unit code sign consisted of a numeral in white (one exception was the red numerals used by

Signals' vehicles) on a coloured square. The actual numerals and colours applicable to most armoured vehicles are summarized in Table 5.

Between 1939 and 1940 the 1st Army Tank Brigade used the unit signs applicable to the 1st Brigade of an armoured division with a white bar added above the sign to denote that it came under Corps command. Subsequently, independent armoured and tank brigades displayed a variety of unit codes. Tank brigades, which replaced the third infantry brigade in the 'mixed' divisions in 1942-43, used the infantry unit codes of 67-68-69 on a brown square.

Other code number sequences used for the three tank units of independent brigades included the following. 6th Guards Tank Brigade, 1944: 152, 153 and 154; 25th Tank Brigade, 1944: 162, 163 and 164; 34th Tank Brigade, 1944: 155, 156 and 157; 21st Tank Brigade: 174, 175 and 176, later 172, 173 and 174; 4th Armoured Brigade, 1944: 122, 123 and 124; 8th Armoured Brigade, 1944: 994, 995 and 996; 31st Tank Brigade, 1944: 991, 992 and 993. The background colour was red for the armoured brigades, but for the tank brigades various one- or two-colour schemes existed. By 1945, however, the 51-52-53 series was used for independent armoured brigades as well as those in armoured divisions.

1st Assault Brigade R.E. had three

▼118

117. Two knocked-out Shermans of 2nd Royal Tank Regiment in Italy. The unit code, 51 in white on a red square, and the 7th Armoured Brigade jerboa both appear low down on the glacis plate level with the track drive sprockets. (I.W.M.)

118. This Stuart belonging to 5th Canadian Armoured Regiment (8th Princess Louise's New Brunswick Hussars) gives a good example of standard British tactical, unit code and formation markings used by Canadian tank units in England in about 1941. The vehicle is carrying the yellow 'C' Squadron sign and the unit code 62 in white on a green square appropriate to the junior armoured brigade (2nd Armoured Brigade) of an armoured division. The 5th Canadian Armoured Division's badge is displayed on the left-hand front track-guard.

▲119

Assault Engineer Regiments (each containing three Assault Squadrons), which carried the unit codes 1233, 1234 and 1235 on a light blue background.

In 1942 British armoured divisions were reorganized to include one armoured brigade (instead of two) and one infantry brigade. The unit codes used by them in the United Kingdom, north-west Europe and the Italian campaign were generally as in Table 6.

The unit code sign was supposed to be painted on the right-hand side of the vehicle (from the driver's viewpoint) at the front and rear, with the formation sign on the left-hand side. However, these instructions were frequently ignored or misinterpreted—by examining the photographs in this book the reader will discover how signs were actually positioned. In the Middle East the unit and brigade signs were often painted in conjunction, one below the other. Both unit and formation signs were officially to be 9½ inches high by 8½ inches wide.

Reconnaissance Corps battalions in British infantry divisions had the unit code 41 in white on a green over blue background. The same colours were also used, the other way up, for Armoured Reconnaissance Regiments in 1943-45. Prior to the formation of the Reconnaissance Corps, Divisional Royal Armoured Corps regiments (which had carried out a similar function in infantry divisions) had the unit code 2 on a black square.

Unit Code Signs used by British Armoured Divisions in Europe and the Middle East, 1939-42				Table 5	
		1939-40 Numerals		1941-42 Numerals	
Armoured Division	Colour	Europe	Middle East	Europe	Middle East
Armoured Car Regiment	(a)	–	14	47	76
HQ (I) Armoured Brigade	Red	3	(c)	50	71
Arm'd Regiment/Battalion (1)	Red	4	24	51	40
Arm'd Regiment/Battalion (2)	Red	5	25	52	86
Arm'd Regiment/Battalion (3)	Red	6	26	53	67
HQ (II) Armoured Brigade	Green	7	(c)	60	(b)
Arm'd Regiment/Battalion (1)	Green	8	28	61	–
Arm'd Regiment/Battalion (2)	Green	9	29	62	–
Arm'd Regiment/Battalion (3)	Green	10	30	63	–

Notes:
(a)   The colour in Europe was black, and white and green are reported to have been used in the Middle East, although this statement is not supported by photographic evidence.
(b)   Armoured brigades that saw action in the desert were frequently switched from one division to another, and unit and formation signs were often omitted. Various unit code numbers were adopted between 1941 and 1942, but eventually the general practice seems to have been to use the 40-86-67 series. However, as brigade and divisional signs were employed in combination with the unit code this served to distinguish between individual units, serving in the same division, which might be displaying the same code number.
(c)   Not ascertained, but probably 23 and 27. The 6th Armoured Division did not show unit code numbers on its AFVs, either in Great Britain or Tunisia, but used instead a coloured patch below the formation sign.

Unit Code Signs used by British Armoured Divisions, 1942-45		Table 6
Armoured Car Regiment	44(a)	
Armoured Reconnaissance Regiment	45(b)	
HQ Armoured Brigade	50	
Armoured Regiment/Battalion (1)	51	
Armoured Regiment/Battalion (2)	52	
Armoured Regiment/Battalion (3)	53	

Notes:
(a)   Originally 47 on a black background and then 44 on a blue/green background. In 1943 became Corps troops until 1945 when they were returned to the armoured divisions.
(b)   A blue/green background. This unit was added in 1943.

119. A parade of Mark VIB light tanks and carriers of 9th Australian Divisional Cavalry Regiment in Syria in 1941. The Division's platypus sign appears on the nearest carrier. (I.W.M.)

120. An unusual position for the unit code sign (41), but no doubt dictated by the wealth of stowage on this Daimler armoured car of 2nd Derbyshire Yeomanry. This unit was, somewhat unusually, Reconnaissance Regiment of 51st Highland Division, whose sign is to the left of the 41 on the turret, in the north-west Europe campaign. (I.W.M.)

121. Humber Mark IV armoured cars of Skinners Horse, the Reconnaissance Regiment of 8th Indian Division (hence the unit code 41) in Italy. The two-colour camouflage is probably green and dark brown. (I.W.M.)

▲120 ▼121

▲122 ▼123

Recognition Markings

In 1940 British tanks in France carried a white square on their hull front, sides and rear as a general recognition mark. Between November 1941 and about March 1942 in the Western Desert, the white/red/white recognition sign of 1918 was revived. This sign (which was 18in. × 18in.) was then superseded by a white St. Andrews cross used on upper surfaces of vehicles as an air recognition mark. This sign was only used for a few months in 1942, it was then replaced by an R.A.F.-type roundel which continued to be used on vehicles in Italy until mid-1943.

In the United Kingdom in 1940, after the evacuation of the British Expeditionary Force from France, a white band was painted around tank turrets (or round the lower hull of turretless armoured vehicles, such as carriers) as a recognition sign. The system was changed in February 1941 when a Cambridge-blue flag (2ft. × 1ft.) was carried, and displayed when it was necessary to establish identity. From about September 1941 a yellow celanese (man-made fabric) triangle was adopted for air identification of tanks, armoured cars and armoured command vehicles equipped with radio. An AFV recognition sign, consisting of a rectangle 10 inches high divided vertically into 6 inch red/white/red strips (apparently intended to be white/red/white as in the Middle East, but a misunderstanding arose) was introduced about March 1942. Officially it continued in use until the spring of 1944 and was carried on all AFVs in the United Kingdom and those of the 1st Army in Tunisia. Later on, its use by all British armoured units in Italy was fairly general. The 'Allied Star' was added to British vehicles from mid-1943 onwards, in preparation for the D-Day landings in 1944. This was a white five-pointed star enclosed in a white ring earlier introduced by the United States forces in the North African landings in 1942—although the white ring was not always used. The star was usually shown only on an upper surface (such as the hull over the engine in Shermans) of British tanks in north-west Europe. However, when used on British and Indian tanks in the 1944-45 Burma campaign the star appeared on the hull and/or turret sides as well.

The same principles as those outlined above applied in general to British Commonwealth armoured units, particularly where these were serving in theatres of war alongside British units. War Department numbers in the British series were allocated to AFVs used by the Canadians and South Africans, although South African armoured cars built specifically for the Union Defence Force had their own numbers and used the prefix

▲124 ▼125

122. Cruiser and light tanks of 1st Royal Tank Regiment in November 1941. The white/red/white recognition signs are particularly prominent. Note that the cruiser still has the 1940-style unit and formation (7th Armoured Division) markings. (I.W.M.)

123. Light tanks showing the white turret band recognition marks used in the United Kingdom during the latter part of 1940. These are Vickers-Carden-Loyd tanks (originally ordered for the Dutch) belonging to 3rd Troop, 'F' Squadron, 2nd Royal Gloucestershire Hussars. (I.W.M.)

124. Conspicuous red/white/red recognition signs on Daimler armoured cars of 1st Derbyshire Yeomanry, 6th Armoured Division, in Tunisia. The white tactical sign (5th Troop, 'C' Squadron) is more widely displayed than was customary, the lower one being liable to confusion with a bridge group sign. Also showing are the unit mobilization number and the divisional sign. (I.W.M.)

125. Clearly painted cruiser tanks of 'A' and 'B' Squadrons, 2nd Royal Tank Regiment, on their way to France in 1940. Visible on the nearest Mark VIA cruiser are the tactical sign of 5th Troop, 'B' Squadron, on the turret; the mobilization number with the associated coloured strips, usually shown on kit bags but more rarely on tanks, on the hull; the W.D. number T 9165; the bridge group sign in black on a plain yellow disc then used on AFVs; the unit code sign in white on a green background; and the 1st Armoured Division rhinoceros.

'U'. The same basic forms of tactical signs were almost universal, with the minor difference that some Canadian units used an inverted triangle as the 'A' Squadron sign. This symbol was also used by some Australian independent tank squadrons in the Pacific theatre of war. Canadian and South African armoured divisions, in Italy and north-west Europe, used the same code signs as those applicable to British armoured divisions of the period. The 4th New Zealand Armoured Brigade in Italy did not conform to this system and used the unit code numerals 91, 80, 52 in white on red squares for the 18th, 19th and 20th New Zealand Armoured Regiments.

Indian armoured divisions and brigades in the Second World War were, in fact, integrated British-Indian formations, and, in general, they adopted the British system. From about mid-1942, the 31st Indian Armoured Division in Persia and Syria used unit codes applicable to contem-porary British formations in the Middle East. Before this date the codes used were 142, 143 and 144. The 44th Indian Armoured Division in India in 1944, on the other hand, had a unique series of unit codes. These were 118, 119 and 120, on a two-colour background, for the three armoured regiments: 116th Regiment, R.A.C., Probyn's Horse and Royal Deccan Horse. By 1945, the conventional series 51, 52, 53 was used, although they retained the two-colour background.

A system adopted by the Australian Army, and used by them in the Pacific in 1945, was that of painting the unit number (not in code) in conjunction with a serial number denoting the type of unit—hence, $\frac{2\text{-}9}{52}$ displayed on a Matilda of 2/9th Armoured Regiment.

Other markings used on British and Commonwealth armoured fighting vehicles in the Second World War were the Bridge Group sign and mobilization serial numbers. The Bridge Group sign was either a black figure on a yellow disc or, more commonly on AFVs later in the War, the less conspicuous form of a black figure (sometimes outlined in yellow) within a yellow ring. This sign indicated that the vehicle was not allowed to cross a bridge with a lower classification number (approximately in tons) and was always displayed at the front of the vehicle. Mobilization serial numbers were allocated to units for shipping purposes and were usually only shown on vehicles shortly before, during and after the voyage. For AFVs tactically loaded on Tank Landing Ships, the L.S.T. number was also often displayed in conjunction with the mobilization serial number. Another variation was that of painting coloured bars (more frequently seen on kit bags) on vehicles plus the mobilization number.

▲126

▼127

126. Cromwell Command/O.P. tanks of 3rd Royal Horse Artillery in a 7th Armoured Division parade in Berlin in 1945. The 'X' sign on the middle tank denotes a Battery Commander's vehicle and the 'RB' on the tank to its right identifies it as the 'B' Troop Commander's. The unit code sign 74, in white on a square divided red over blue, is combined with the jerboa divisional sign. (I.W.M.)

127. A Mark VIB light tank used as an Observation Post vehicle by 'B' Battery, 1st Royal Horse Artillery, whose chequer sign appears on the turret side, in the Western Desert, 1940. (I.W.M.)

AFV CAMOUFLAGE COLOURS

Armoured cars used by the Royal Naval Air Service in 1914-15 were generally finished in a light or medium shade of naval grey. An exception was the Royal Marine Artillery Anti-Aircraft Brigade's Pierce-Arrow armoured cars (with 2pdr. 'pom-pom' AA guns) supplied in 1915; these were painted 'Daimler khaki-green, in accordance with Admiralty specifications. There is reason to believe that other R.N.A.S. armoured cars shared this colour.

The first British Mark I tanks rolled off the assembly line in a standard grey finish, and it was left to Lt. Col. Solomon J. Solomon (who was a peace-time artist) of the Royal Engineers, to design and, with the aid of a detachment of men, paint a camouflage scheme on the tanks. Solomon's system consisted of patches of red, green, blue and brown and was used on the first tanks in action on the Somme in 1916. Hereafter, this scheme fell by the wayside and in most cases the tanks were left plain grey. Towards the end of the Great War, a type of khaki-green (probably similar to the Admiralty's Daimler khaki-green) or khaki-brown—described as 'a neutral brown colour' came into use. Disruptive patches of colour were sometimes used on both Rolls-Royce and Lanchester armoured cars in France around 1916 and 1917. This was often in a more jagged form than was usually seen on tanks in 1916, boundaries between the different colours being frequently outlined in a dark shade. Field and medium artillery also often adopted this camouflage style.

Immediately following the First World War the grey, brown and khaki-green colours continued in use. In 1930 this khaki-green was known as bronze-green and was published in British Standard No. 381-1930 as: Colours No. 22 Light Bronze Green; No. 23 Middle Bronze Green; and No. 24 Deep Bronze Green. No. 23 appears to have been the one for normal use in the United Kingdom, with No. 22 for use in terrain with light foliage; and No. 24 for dark surroundings. A range of Brunswick greens also appears to have been used.

The 5th Battalion Royal Tank Corps experimented with various colour schemes in the inter-war period, including a three or

▲128 ▼129

128. A three-colour camouflage scheme tried out on a Mark II Medium by 5th Battalion Royal Tank Corps in England during the 1930s. The three colours, which were probably a middle or deep bronze-green with possibly a lighter green and a sand colour, are outlined in black.

129. Part of the light camouflage scheme on this Grant of 22nd Armoured Brigade, seen here in the Desert in 1944, doubling-up as a blackboard. This scheme of three colours outlined in black obviously has much in common with that tried out by 5th Battalion, Royal Tank Regiment, some ten years earlier, but a similar form was also used by the French up to 1940. (I.W.M.)

130. Sherman tanks of 'C' Squadron, The Queen's Bays, in Tunisia. The camouflage is sand colour with a darker shade of grey or possibly even pink. The unit sign 40, in white on a red background, is stencilled on the front track-guard in combination with the rhinoceros, which here represents 2nd Armoured Brigade, 1st Armoured Division. Note the side rails for the attachment of 'sun shields'. (I.W.M.)

131. A Churchill in Egypt, 1942, fitted with its 'sun shield' lorry camouflage. Only a handful of Churchills were with the 8th Army, but most tanks were equipped with a similar form of disguise. (R. J. Icks)

▲131

132. Two Churchills of 142nd Regiment, R.A.C., in Tunisia. The mottled camouflage on the farthest tank, a lighter colour applied over the basic dark green, appears to be fairly well suited to this terrain. (I.W.M.)

133. 9th Queen's Royal Lancers in the Desert in 1942. The more patchy application of the camouflage pattern may be contrasted with the more flowing style of the Bays in the same brigade. On the rear track-guards of the nearest tank are the number 86 in white on a red square, and the 1st Armoured Division sign (censored in this photograph) also in white. The tactical troop sign shown on the stowage bin would have been in yellow. (I.W.M.)

▲132

four colour disruptive pattern with dark outlines; and a scheme consisting of a plain colour, with a narrow, dark, horizontal band around the middle of the hull.

The early inter-war years found those armoured car companies of the R.T.C. in India usually adopting dark grey or silver grey for their vehicles—the latter shade was used during the hot season. In 1936, the 2nd Light Tank Company was using khaki (sand colour) or light green for its tanks. A disruptive pattern in darker shades, as appropriate, was sometimes added. These schemes were probably representative of other armoured units in India during the same period.

In mid-1939 the War Office laid down instructions for vehicle camouflage to be in disruptive patterns in two colours. These were based on three shades: namely G.3, also known as Khaki Green No. 3; Middle Bronze Green, No. 23 in B.S. 381-1930; G.4, Dark Green No. 4, Deep Bronze Green, No. 24, B.S. 381-1930; and G.5 Light Green No. 5, Light Bronze Green, No. 22, B.S. 381-1930. The standard overall colour was to be G.3—the medium colour, and for average European conditions the disruptive patches (to be painted with a diagonal or horizontal trend) were to be in dark green G.4. The dark colour was to predominate on upper light-reflecting surfaces to help avoid detection from the air, and the light green could be used for the disruptive patches when a lighter effect was required for light backgrounds. Three colours could be authorized in certain circumstances, but this usage was not common in Europe.

During 1941 a khaki-brown shade (similar to that of battledress uniform) was again used for tanks, although the colour does not seem to have been officially recognized until November of that year. The War Office then authorized its use as an alternative to Khaki Green No. 3. The khaki-brown mentioned was known as Standard Camouflage Colour No. 2, and was included in British Standard 987C published in September 1942. Also included in B.S.1 987C was a very dark brown disruptive colour specified as Standard Camouflage Colour No. 1A. By 1942 the khaki-green colour seems to have been standardized as 'Shade No. 7' a colour mid-way between the earlier khaki-greens Nos. 3 and 5. The fact is, however, that in the United Kingdom in 1942-43 khaki-brown (which also appeared in a lighter form as shade No. 4, and it seems took a pinky tinge) predominated, and, quite frequently the disruptive patches were not used. Photographs of some Churchills used for training in 1942 seem to indicate that they were finished in an overall medium grey.

Because of a War Office instruction in 1944 that khaki-green was to replace Standard Colour No. 2, it again became the most common shade for AFVs in north-west Europe. Khaki-green shade No. 15 was standardized as an ammendment to B.S.987C-1942, and officially known as Olive Drab. This colour was only slightly different from shade No. 7 (mentioned above), and with weathering it is unlikely that the difference would have been evident. (British Olive Drab was similar to the U.S. Army Engineers' standard camouflage colour of the same name.)

In Egypt in 1939, British AFVs were generally painted in a sand colour, but the exact shade used is not certain. It was probably No. 61 in B.S. No. 381-1930, known as Light Stone; but it might have been either No. 52 or No. 53, which were Pale Cream and Deep Cream respectively. Where a darker disruptive colour was used it appears that this may have been a Slate Grey (No. 34, B.S.381). The 11th Hussars have recorded that in 1937 their armoured cars were painted in a new desert camouflage scheme of deep red (possibly terra cotta, No. 44, B.S.381-1930, continued in a similar shade as No. 11A in B.S.987C-1942) and sand colour. In 1940, a scheme apparently intended to confuse enemy gunners, rather than for concealment (generally impractical in the open Desert terrain where movement raised dust clouds), was adopted. This consisted of radiating diagonal bands of colour—the shades generally being sand, light grey and slate grey in that order—from the bottom upwards (B.S.381-1930, Nos. 61 or 64, 28 and 34 respectively). Also at this time, and after the radiating pattern had been dropped, these shades were used in various combinations in irregular patterns.

Different regiments in the Desert have recorded that their vehicles were painted yellow and grey, dull grey black, 'sand and green' (a motor battalion); light yellow faded to a pale beige; and 'desert grey'. In fact, the effects of North African sun and sand scouring soon changed colours out of all recognition. Hodson's Horse, an Indian regiment, had tanks in Paiforce (Persia/Iraq) which were described as a 'dull pinkish colour, rather like the shade of light coloured bricks'.

As will be gathered there was little uniformity in camouflage painting in the Middle East. In about May 1941 the 22nd Armoured Brigade adopted a unique form of dazzle painting, using, instead of paint, a form of cement rendering in black, white and brown. To this were also added the 'sun shields' common to other formations in the Desert at this time. This device consisted of canvas on steel tubes, to help make tanks look like lorries from the air.

▲134 ▼135 136▶

134. A Daimler armoured car of an unidentified regiment showing the large serial number which was used by Movement Control troops in the deception plan before the Battle of Alamein in October 1942. (I.W.M.)

135. Dark spots were added to the two-colour camouflage scheme of this Sherman, *Sheik*, of the Royal Scots Greys, in Sicily. The pattern was still being used when this photograph was taken near Mount Vesuvius in 1943. (I.W.M.)

136. Malta camouflage—the reason for this form of camouflage on a Mark VIC light tank of the Independent Tank Squadron in Malta is explained by the stone wall behind it. (I.W.M.)

▲137 ▼138

The lorry effect was heightened by the 7th Hussars, and some other regiments equipped with Mark IV cruisers or Crusaders (both of which had large wheels), who painted the inner pairs of wheels a dark colour—thus leaving the light coloured wheels in the approximate position for a four or six-wheeled lorry. As part of the overall deception before the Alamein battle in October 1942, 722 'sun shields' were placed in position and later occupied by tanks and other AFVs and weapons moved in by night to avoid air detection. These 'hides' were numbered and the AFVs or guns were given corresponding numbers. Numbers (examples for the 9th Lancers are 1038, 324) were sometimes carried on the AFVs in black figures on a white rectangular plate to help Movement Control staff. A scheme devised by Major Jasper Maskelyne, R.E., (who had been a stage magician in peacetime) for the Armoured Command Vehicles of 7th Armoured Division, was later more widely adopted in the Desert: with paint and canvas the ACV was disguised as an AEC lorry.

British and Indian tank units fighting in Burma were painted 'jungle green', which was a very dark olive green, even darker than olive drab, included in B.S.987C—1942, as shade No. 13. (It was replaced in July 1945 by the slightly darker shade No. 16.) Australian tank units did fight in the jungles of New Guinea, but the 14th Army's Burma campaign was fought on open terrain and the hot sun soon faded the dark green to a light shade. In Australia, both before the War and during its early years, AFVs were painted deep bronze-green; later, a three-colour camouflage system more appropriate to the Australian terrain was devised.

137. Desert camouflage in an English winter, December 1941. A Valentine, accompanied by a carrier and scout car, of 40th Royal Tank Regiment shortly before embarking for the Middle East. It is painted all over sand colour and track sand shields are fitted. (I.W.M.)

138. Valentines of the 17th/21st Lancers lined up for a review by the King in 1941. The nearest tanks belong to 1st, 2nd and 3rd Troops of 'A' Squadron. Note the thin triangles and figures of the tactical signs of this regiment. Middle bronze-green with disruptive patches of deep bronze-green is the camouflage used here. (I.W.M.)

139

140

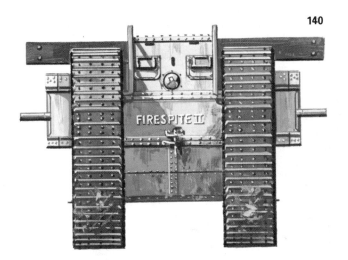

139. *No. 8 Squadron, Royal Naval Air Service Armoured Car Division.* A Rolls-Royce Armoured Car (1914 pattern) of 'C' Section, about early 1915. This car is shown in 'Daimler khaki-green' with red letters for 'RNAS' and the Squadron symbols. The small raised metal plate on which the car's name appears is just above the 'C' of '8-C-2' at the rear. The White Ensign was normally only flown on ceremonial occasions.

140-141. *'F' Battalion, Tank Corps.* Two views of a Mark IV Female tank—F.1, *Firespite II*—shown during a training period in October 1917. The overall grey finish shown was often used at this time, although the red lines were added by the unit. The playing card symbols may have been copied from the French, who used them frequently on their tanks.

141

142. *4th/7th Royal Dragoon Guards.* A Mark VIB light tank of 1st Troop, 'B' Squadron, in France in 1940, when the Regiment was the Divisional Royal Armoured Corps Regiment for 2nd Infantry Division. The tank is shown in light bronze-green with disruptive patches of middle bronze-green. The standard colours for tactical signs do not appear to have been adopted by all cavalry regiments at this time. The AFV recognition mark—a white square—appears on the hull side.

142

143. *15th/19th The King's Royal Hussars.* A Mark V, Covenanter II Cruiser tank of 1st Troop, 'A' Squadron, in England in 1941. This unit was then the second regiment in 28th Armoured Brigade of 9th Armoured Division. The tank is shown in khaki-brown with disruptive patches of very dark brown—Standard Camouflage Colours Nos. 2 and 1A, respectively.

143

144. *6th Royal Tank Regiment.* A Mark I Cruiser in the Western Desert in 1940. This picture shows the camouflage scheme of radiating lines used by 6th and 1st Royal Tank Regiments and other units at the time. The lightest colour was usually at the bottom—to lighten shadows in the suspension—and the darkest on top, where it would lessen the contrast of reflected light. It was the practice in 6th Royal Tank Regiment to show the tank's name on the rear of the turret, and the divisional sign (7th Armoured Division) and unit code sign ('30' in white on a green rectangle) on the front and rear of the track-guards.

144

145-146. *3rd Battalion Reconnaissance Corps.* Two views of a Universal Carrier of the 9th Platoon (or Troop) of 'C' Company (or Squadron) in England in 1941. This unit formed part of 3rd Division, whose sign is on the offside front track-guard. The Carrier is shown in camouflage that was common at this time—khaki-brown with very dark brown disruptive patches. The Company (or Squadron) sign, shown on the side of the hull, was, however, unique to 3rd Battalion Reconnaissance Corps. Bridge group numbers were not displayed by this unit in 1941, but were added by 1942.

145

146

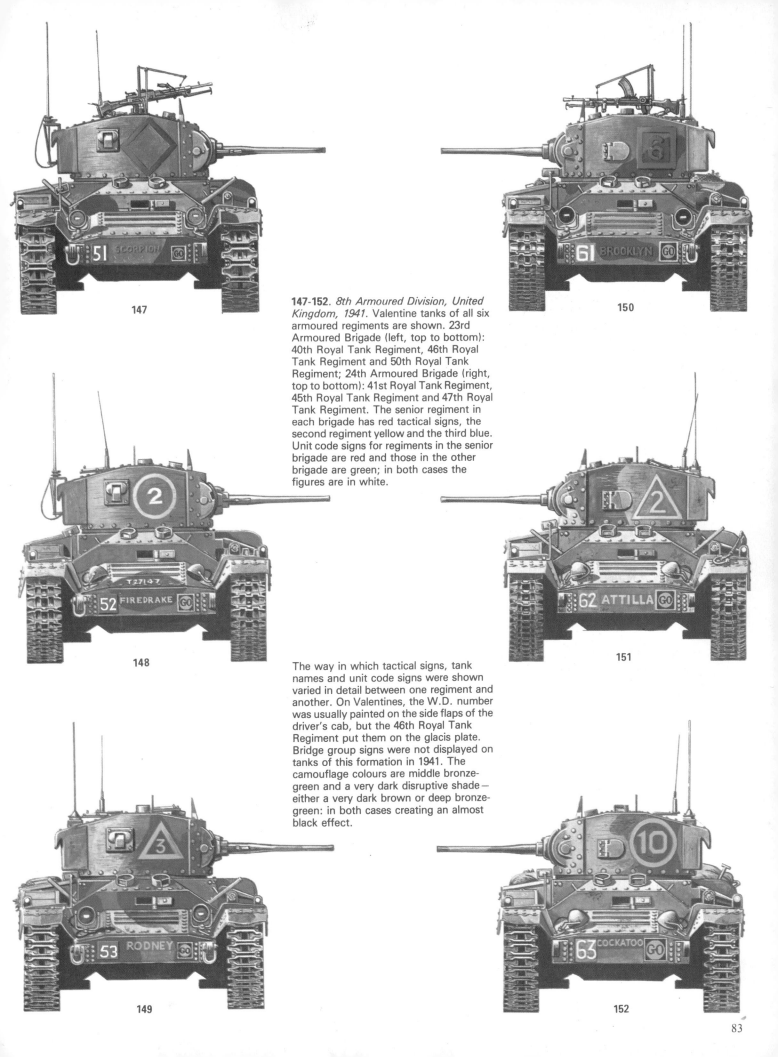

147

150

147-152. *8th Armoured Division, United Kingdom, 1941.* Valentine tanks of all six armoured regiments are shown. 23rd Armoured Brigade (left, top to bottom): 40th Royal Tank Regiment, 46th Royal Tank Regiment and 50th Royal Tank Regiment; 24th Armoured Brigade (right, top to bottom): 41st Royal Tank Regiment, 45th Royal Tank Regiment and 47th Royal Tank Regiment. The senior regiment in each brigade has red tactical signs, the second regiment yellow and the third blue. Unit code signs for regiments in the senior brigade are red and those in the other brigade are green; in both cases the figures are in white.

148

151

The way in which tactical signs, tank names and unit code signs were shown varied in detail between one regiment and another. On Valentines, the W.D. number was usually painted on the side flaps of the driver's cab, but the 46th Royal Tank Regiment put them on the glacis plate. Bridge group signs were not displayed on tanks of this formation in 1941. The camouflage colours are middle bronze-green and a very dark disruptive shade—either a very dark brown or deep bronze-green: in both cases creating an almost black effect.

149

152

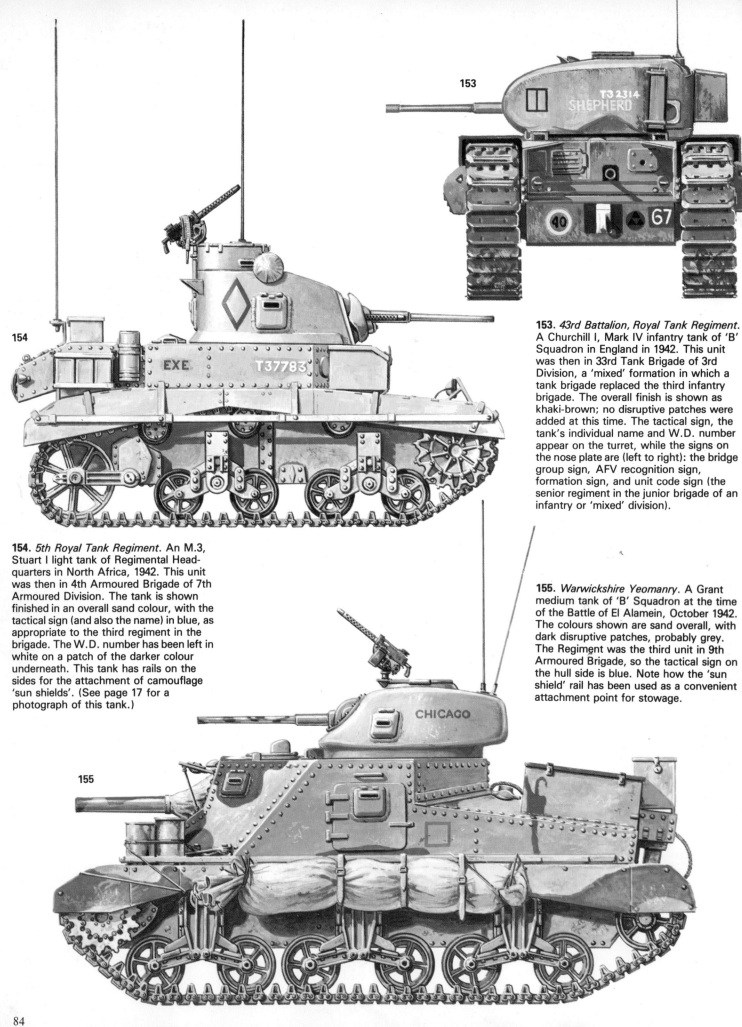

153. *43rd Battalion, Royal Tank Regiment.* A Churchill I, Mark IV infantry tank of 'B' Squadron in England in 1942. This unit was then in 33rd Tank Brigade of 3rd Division, a 'mixed' formation in which a tank brigade replaced the third infantry brigade. The overall finish is shown as khaki-brown; no disruptive patches were added at this time. The tactical sign, the tank's individual name and W.D. number appear on the turret, while the signs on the nose plate are (left to right): the bridge group sign, AFV recognition sign, formation sign, and unit code sign (the senior regiment in the junior brigade of an infantry or 'mixed' division).

154. *5th Royal Tank Regiment.* An M.3, Stuart I light tank of Regimental Headquarters in North Africa, 1942. This unit was then in 4th Armoured Brigade of 7th Armoured Division. The tank is shown finished in an overall sand colour, with the tactical sign (and also the name) in blue, as appropriate to the third regiment in the brigade. The W.D. number has been left in white on a patch of the darker colour underneath. This tank has rails on the sides for the attachment of camouflage 'sun shields'. (See page 17 for a photograph of this tank.)

155. *Warwickshire Yeomanry.* A Grant medium tank of 'B' Squadron at the time of the Battle of El Alamein, October 1942. The colours shown are sand overall, with dark disruptive patches, probably grey. The Regiment was the third unit in 9th Armoured Brigade, so the tactical sign on the hull side is blue. Note how the 'sun shield' rail has been used as a convenient attachment point for stowage.

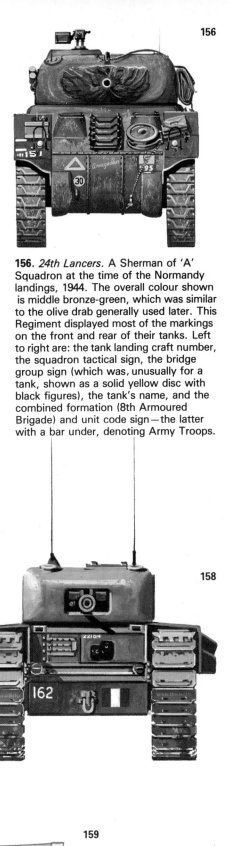

156. *24th Lancers.* A Sherman of 'A' Squadron at the time of the Normandy landings, 1944. The overall colour shown is middle bronze-green, which was similar to the olive drab generally used later. This Regiment displayed most of the markings on the front and rear of their tanks. Left to right are: the tank landing craft number, the squadron tactical sign, the bridge group sign (which was, unusually for a tank, shown as a solid yellow disc with black figures), the tank's name, and the combined formation (8th Armoured Brigade) and unit code sign—the latter with a bar under, denoting Army Troops.

157. *3rd King's Own Hussars.* A Sherman of 'A' Squadron in Syria in 1943, where, with the rest of 9th Armoured Brigade, the Regiment was re-built after heavy losses sustained at the Battle of Alamein. Close co-operation with the 2nd New Zealand Division in North Africa is commemorated by the fern leaf symbol on the hull side. The camouflage colours shown are a reminder that not all 'sand' is yellow: Petra, in neighbouring Jordan, was called the 'rose red city'. The formation and unit code signs on the glacis plate are shown combined as was usual in the Middle East at this time.

158. *51st Royal Tank Regiment.* A Churchill IV in Italy, 1944, when the 51st Royal Tank Regiment was the second unit in 25th Tank Brigade. It is shown in the bronze-green colour also used earlier in Tunisia. The unit code sign and the AFV recognition sign are on the nose plate. The unit mobilization number (22164) is shown next to the driver's hatch.

159. *3rd (Tank) Battalion Scots Guards.* A Churchill III in the United Kingdom, 1943. This is the Left Flank Squadron Leader's tank. Shown finished in overall khaki-brown, it has the AFV recognition sign, the W.D. number (the suffix 'B' denoting a re-work) and the name 'Esk' on the hull side; the tactical sign is on the turret. The front of the hull had the 2nd Army sign and the unit code sign 154 with a white bar below denoting Troops (the 6th Guards Tank Brigade) under Army command.

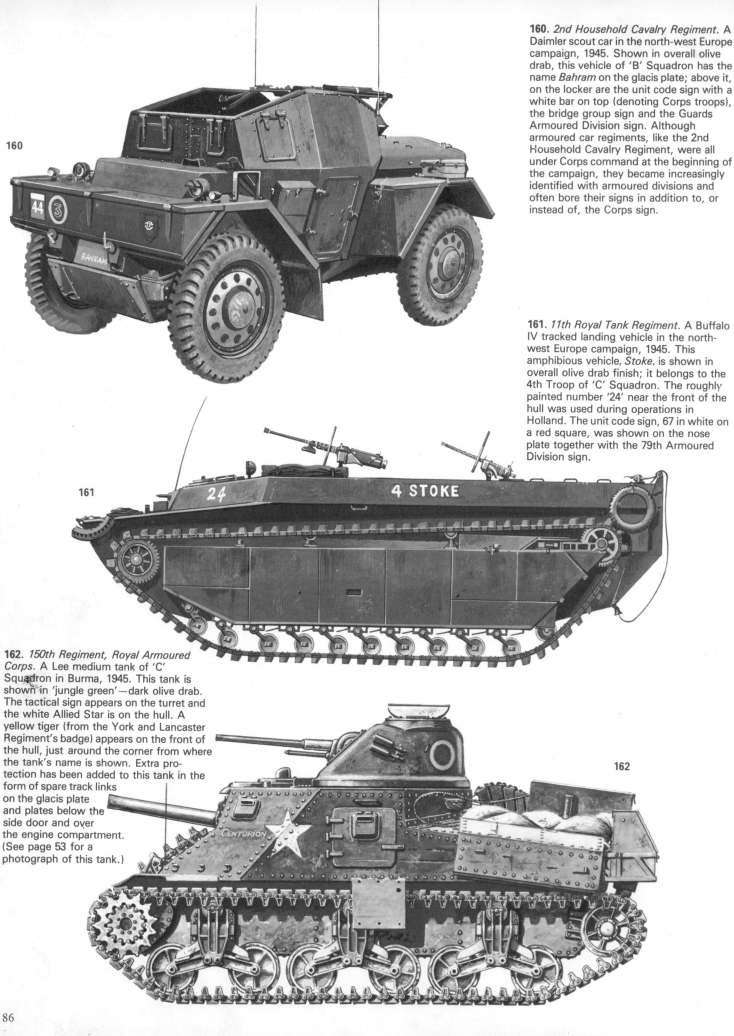

160. *2nd Household Cavalry Regiment.* A Daimler scout car in the north-west Europe campaign, 1945. Shown in overall olive drab, this vehicle of 'B' Squadron has the name *Bahram* on the glacis plate; above it, on the locker are the unit code sign with a white bar on top (denoting Corps troops), the bridge group sign and the Guards Armoured Division sign. Although armoured car regiments, like the 2nd Household Cavalry Regiment, were all under Corps command at the beginning of the campaign, they became increasingly identified with armoured divisions and often bore their signs in addition to, or instead of, the Corps sign.

161. *11th Royal Tank Regiment.* A Buffalo IV tracked landing vehicle in the north-west Europe campaign, 1945. This amphibious vehicle, *Stoke*, is shown in overall olive drab finish; it belongs to the 4th Troop of 'C' Squadron. The roughly painted number '24' near the front of the hull was used during operations in Holland. The unit code sign, 67 in white on a red square, was shown on the nose plate together with the 79th Armoured Division sign.

162. *150th Regiment, Royal Armoured Corps.* A Lee medium tank of 'C' Squadron in Burma, 1945. This tank is shown in 'jungle green'—dark olive drab. The tactical sign appears on the turret and the white Allied Star is on the hull. A yellow tiger (from the York and Lancaster Regiment's badge) appears on the front of the hull, just around the corner from where the tank's name is shown. Extra protection has been added to this tank in the form of spare track links on the glacis plate and plates below the side door and over the engine compartment. (See page 53 for a photograph of this tank.)

163. Guards Armoured Division.

164. 1st Armoured Division.

165. 2nd Armoured Division.

166. 6th Armoured Division.

167. 7th Armoured Division.

168. 8th Armoured Division.

169. 9th Armoured Division.

170. 10th Armoured Division.

171. 11th Armoured Division.

172. 42nd Armoured Division.

173. 79th Armoured Division.

174. 4th Armoured Brigade.

175. 6th Guards Tank Brigade.

176. 7th Armoured Brigade.

177. 8th Armoured Brigade.

178. 9th Armoured Brigade.

179. 21st Armoured Brigade.

180. 22nd Armoured Brigade.

181. 23rd Armoured Brigade.

182. 25th Armoured Brigade.

183. 25th Army Tank Brigade (later 25th Armoured Engineer Brigade).

184. 27th Armoured Brigade.

185. 33rd Armoured Brigade.

186. 34th Armoured Brigade.

187. 5th Canadian Armoured Division.

188. 1st Canadian Armoured Brigade.

189. 2nd Canadian Armoured Brigade.

190. 4th Australian Armoured Brigade.

191. 31st Indian Armoured Division.

192. 44th Indian Armoured Division.

193. 2nd New Zealand Division (which included an armoured brigade).

194. 6th South African Armoured Division.